Glencoe Mathematics

Geometry

Chapter 10
Resource Masters

New York, New York Columbus, Ohio Chicago, Illinois Peoria, Illinois Woodland Hills, California

Consumable Workbooks Many of the worksheets contained in the Chapter Resource Masters are available as consumable workbooks in both English and Spanish.

	ISBN10	ISBN13
Study Guide and Intervention Workbook	0-07-877344-X	978-0-07-877344-0
Skills Practice Workbook	0-07-877346-6	978-0-07-877346-4
Practice Workbook	0-07-877347-4	978-0-07-877347-1
Word Problem Practice Workbook	0-07-877349-0	978-0-07-877349-5

Spanish Versions

Study Guide and Intervention Workbook	0-07-877345-8	978-0-07-877345-7
Practice Workbook	0-07-877348-2	978-0-07-877348-8

Answers for Workbooks The answers for Chapter 10 of these workbooks can be found in the back of this Chapter Resource Masters booklet.

StudentWorks Plus™ This CD-ROM includes the entire Student Edition test along with the English workbooks listed above.

TeacherWorks Plus™ All of the materials found in this booklet are included for viewing, printing, and editing in this CD-ROM.

Spanish Assessment Masters (ISBN10: 0-07-877350-4, ISBN13: 978-0-07-877350-1) These masters contain a Spanish version of Chapter 10 Test Form 2A and Form 2C.

 **Glencoe**

The **McGraw·Hill** Companies

Send all inquiries to:
Glencoe/McGraw-Hill
8787 Orion Place
Columbus, OH 43240

ISBN13: 978-0-07-873967-5
ISBN10: 0-07-873967-5

Geometry CRM10

Printed in the United States of America

2 3 4 5 6 7 8 9 10 009 13 12 11 10 09 08 07

CONTENTS

Teacher's Guide to Using the
Chapter 10 Resource Masters

The *Chapter 10 Resource Masters* includes the core materials needed for Chapter 10. These materials include worksheets, extensions, and assessment options. The answers for these pages appear at the back of this booklet.

All of the materials found in this booklet are included for viewing and printing on the *TeacherWorks Plus*™ CD-ROM.

Chapter Resources

Student-Built Glossary (pages 1–2) These masters are a student study tool that presents up to twenty of the key vocabulary terms from the chapter. Students are to record definitions and/or examples for each term. You may suggest that students highlight or star the terms with which they are not familiar. Give this to students before beginning Lesson 10-1. Encourage them to add these pages to their mathematics study notebooks. Remind them to complete the appropriate words as they study each lesson.

Anticipation Guide (pages 7–8) This master, presented in both English and Spanish, is a survey used before beginning the chapter to pinpoint what students may or may not know about the concepts in the chapter. Students will revisit this survey after they complete the chapter to see if their perceptions have changed.

Lesson Resources

Lesson Reading Guide Get Ready for the Lesson extends the discussion from the beginning of the Student Edition lesson. Read the Lesson asks students to interpret the context of and relationships among terms in the lesson. Finally, Remember What You Learned asks students to summarize what they have learned using various representation techniques. Use as a study tool for note taking or as an informal reading assignment. It is also a helpful tool for ELL (English Language Learners).

Study Guide and Intervention These masters provide vocabulary, key concepts, additional worked-out examples and Check Your Progress exercises to use as a reteaching activity. It can also be used in conjunction with the Student Edition as an instructional tool for students who have been absent.

Skills Practice This master focuses more on the computational nature of the lesson. Use as an additional practice option or as homework for second-day teaching of the lesson.

Practice This master closely follows the types of problems found in the Exercises section of the Student Edition and includes word problems. Use as an additional practice option or as homework for second-day teaching of the lesson.

Word Problem Practice This master includes additional practice in solving word problems that apply the concepts of the lesson. Use as an additional practice or as homework for second-day teaching of the lesson.

Enrichment These activities may extend the concepts of the lesson, offer a historical or multicultural look at the concepts, or widen students' perspectives on the mathematics they are learning. They are written for use with all levels of students.

Graphing Calculator, Scientific Calculator, or Spreadsheet Activities
These activities present ways in which technology can be used with the concepts in some lessons of this chapter. Use as an alternative approach to some concepts or as an integral part of your lesson presentation.

Assessment Options
The assessment masters in the *Chapter 10 Resource Masters* offer a wide range of assessment tools for formative (monitoring) assessment and summative (final) assessment.

Student Recording Sheet This master corresponds with the standardized test practice at the end of the chapter.

Pre-AP Rubric This master provides information for teachers and students on how to assess performance on open-ended questions.

Quizzes Four free-response quizzes offer assessment at appropriate intervals in the chapter.

Mid-Chapter Test This 1-page test provides an option to assess the first half of the chapter. It parallels the timing of the Mid-Chapter Quiz in the Student Edition and includes both multiple-choice and free-response questions.

Vocabulary Test This test is suitable for all students. It includes a list of vocabulary words and 10 questions to assess students' knowledge of those words. This can also be used in conjunction with one of the leveled chapter tests.

Leveled Chapter Tests
- *Form 1* contains multiple-choice questions and is intended for use with below grade level students.
- *Forms 2A and 2B* contain multiple-choice questions aimed at on grade level students. These tests are similar in format to offer comparable testing situations.
- *Forms 2C and 2D* contain free-response questions aimed at on grade level students. These tests are similar in format to offer comparable testing situations.
- *Form 3* is a free-response test for use with above grade level students.

All of the above mentioned tests include a free-response Bonus question.

Extended-Response Test Performance assessment tasks are suitable for all students. Sample answers and a scoring rubric are included for evaluation.

Standardized Test Practice These three pages are cumulative in nature. It includes three parts: multiple-choice questions with bubble-in answer format, griddable questions with answer grids, and short-answer free-response questions.

Answers
- The answers for the Anticipation Guide and Lesson Resources are provided as reduced pages with answers appearing in red.
- Full-size answer keys are provided for the assessment masters.

10 Student-Built Glossary

This is an alphabetical list of the key vocabulary terms you will learn in Chapter 10. As you study the chapter, complete each term's definition or description. Remember to add the page number where you found the term. Add these pages to your Geometry Study Notebook to review vocabulary at the end of the chapter.

Vocabulary Term	Found on Page	Definition/Description/Example
arc		
center		
central angle		
chord		
circle		
circumference		
circumscribed		
diameter		
inscribed		

(continued on the next page)

Chapter Resources

10 Student-Built Glossary *(continued)*

Vocabulary Term	Found on Page	Definition/Description/Example
intercepted		
major arc		
minor arc		
pi (π)		
point of tangency		
radius		
secant		
semicircle		
tangent		

10 Anticipation Guide

Circles and Circumference

Chapter Resources

Step 1 *Before you begin Chapter 10*

- Read each statement.
- Decide whether you Agree (A) or Disagree (D) with the statement.
- Write A or D in the first column OR if you are not sure whether you agree or disagree, write NS (Not Sure).

STEP 1 A, D, or NS	Statement	STEP 2 A or D
	1. The distance from any point on a circle to the center of the circle is called the diameter.	
	2. A chord of a circle is any segment with endpoints that are on the circle.	
	3. The formula for the circumference of a circle is $C = \pi r^2$.	
	4. The vertex of a central angle of a circle is at the center of the circle.	
	5. If two arcs from two different circles have the same measure then the arcs are congruent.	
	6. In a circle, two minor arcs are congruent if their corresponding chords are congruent.	
	7. In a circle, two chords that are equidistant from the center are congruent.	
	8. The measure of an inscribed angle equals the measure of its intercepted arc.	
	9. A line is tangent to a circle only if it contains a chord of the circle.	
	10. Two secant lines of a circle can intersect in the interior or the exterior of the circle.	
	11. If two chords intersect inside a circle then the two chords are congruent.	
	12. The center of a circle represented by the equation $(x + 3)^2 + (y + 5)^2 = 9$ is located at $(3, 5)$.	

Step 2 *After you complete Chapter 10*

- Reread each statement and complete the last column by entering an A or a D.
- Did any of your opinions about the statements change from the first column?
- For those statements that you mark with a D, use a piece of paper to write an example of why you disagree.

10 Ejercicios preparatorios
Círculos

PASO 1 *Antes de comenzar el Capítulo 10*

- Lee cada enunciado.
- Decide si estás de acuerdo (A) o en desacuerdo (D) con el enunciado.
- Escribe A o D en la primera columna O si no estás seguro(a) de la respuesta, escribe NS (No estoy seguro(a).

PASO 1 A, D o NS	Enunciado	PASO 2 A o D
	1. La distancia desde cualquier punto de un círculo al centro del mismo se llama diámetro.	
	2. La cuerda de un círculo es cualquier segmento cuyos extremos están sobre el círculo.	
	3. La fórmula para la circunferencia del círculo es $C = \pi r^2$.	
	4. El vértice del ángulo central de un círculo está en el centro del círculo.	
	5. Si dos arcos de dos círculos diferentes tienen la misma medida, entonces los arcos son congruentes.	
	6. En un círculo, dos arcos menores son congruentes si sus cuerdas correspondientes son congruentes.	
	7. En un círculo, dos cuerdas que equidistan del centro son congruentes.	
	8. La medida de un ángulo inscrito es igual a la medida de la intersección de su arco.	
	9. Una recta es tangente a un círculo sólo si contiene una cuerda del círculo.	
	10. Dos secantes de un círculo se pueden intersecar en el interior o en el exterior del círculo.	
	11. Si dos cuerdas se intersecan dentro de un círculo, entonces las dos cuerdas son congruentes.	
	12. El centro de un círculo que se representa con la ecuación $(x + 3)^2 + (y + 5)^2 = 9$ se localiza en $(3, 5)$.	

PASO 2 *Después de completar el Capítulo 10*

- Vuelve a leer cada enunciado y completa la última columna con una A o una D.
- ¿Cambió cualquiera de tus opiniones sobre los enunciados de la primera columna?
- En una hoja de papel aparte, escribe un ejemplo de por qué estás en desacuerdo con los enunciados que marcaste con una D.

Lesson Reading Guide

Circles and Circumference

Get Ready for the Lesson

Read the introduction to Lesson 10-1 in your textbook.

How could you measure the approximate distance around the circular carousel using everyday measuring devices?

Read the Lesson

1. Refer to the figure.

   a. Name the circle.

   b. Name four radii of the circle.

   c. Name a diameter of the circle.

   d. Name two chords of the circle.

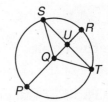

2. Match each description from the first column with the best term from the second column. (Some terms in the second column may be used more than once or not at all.)

   a. a segment other than the diameter endpoints on a circle

   b. the set of all points in a plane that are the same distance from a given point

   c. the distance between the center of a circle and any point on the circle

   d. a chord that passes through the center of a circle

   e. a segment whose endpoints are the center and any point on a circle

   f. a chord made up of two collinear radii

   g. the distance around a circle

   i. radius

   ii. diameter

   iii. chord

   iv. circle

   v. circumference

3. Which equations correctly express a relationship in a circle?

   A. $d = 2r$ **B.** $C = \pi r$ **C.** $C = 2d$ **D.** $d = \dfrac{C}{\pi}$

   E. $r = \dfrac{d}{\pi}$ **F.** $C = r^2$ **G.** $C = 2\pi r$ **H.** $d = \dfrac{1}{2}r$

Remember What You Learned

4. A good way to remember a new geometric term is to relate the word or its parts to geometric terms you already know. Look up the origins of the two parts of the word *diameter* in your dictionary. Explain the meaning of each part and give a term you already know that shares the origin of that part.

5   *Glencoe Geometry*

10-1 Study Guide and Intervention

Circles and Circumference

Parts of Circles A **circle** consists of all points in a plane that are a given distance, called the **radius**, from a given point called the **center**.

A segment or line can intersect a circle in several ways.

- A segment with endpoints that are the center of the circle and a point of the circle is a **radius**.
- A segment with endpoints that lie on the circle is a **chord**.
- A chord that contains the circle's center is a **diameter**.

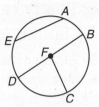

chord: $\overline{AE}$, $\overline{BD}$
radius: $\overline{FB}$, $\overline{FC}$, $\overline{FD}$
diameter: $\overline{BD}$

Example

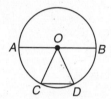

a. Name the circle.
The name of the circle is $\odot O$.

b. Name radii of the circle.
$\overline{AO}$, $\overline{BO}$, $\overline{CO}$, and $\overline{DO}$ are radii.

c. Name chords of the circle.
$\overline{AB}$ and $\overline{CD}$ are chords.

d. Name a diameter of the circle.
$\overline{AB}$ is a diameter.

Exercises

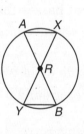

1. Name the circle.

2. Name radii of the circle.

3. Name chords of the circle.

4. Name diameters of the circle.

5. Find AR if AB is 18 millimeters.

6. Find AR and AB if RY is 10 inches.

7. Is $\overline{AB} \cong \overline{XY}$? Explain.

10-1 Study Guide and Intervention *(continued)*

Circles and Circumference

Circumference The **circumference** of a circle is the distance around the circle.

Circumference	For a circumference of C units and a diameter of d units or a radius of r units, $C = \pi d$ or $C = 2\pi r$.

Example Find the circumference of the circle to the nearest hundredth.

13 cm

$C = 2\pi r$ Circumference formula

$\quad = 2\pi(13)$ $r = 13$

$\quad \approx 81.68$ Use a calculator.

The circumference is about 81.68 centimeters.

Exercises

Find the circumference of a circle with the given radius or diameter. Round to the nearest hundredth.

1. $r = 8$ cm

2. $r = 3\sqrt{2}$ ft

3. $r = 4.1$ cm

4. $d = 10$ in.

5. $d = \dfrac{1}{3}$ m

6. $d = 18$ yd

The radius, diameter, or circumference of a circle is given. Find the missing measures to the nearest hundredth.

7. $r = 4$ cm

    $d =$ _____, $C =$ _____

8. $d = 6$ ft

    $r =$ _____, $C =$ _____

9. $r = 12$ cm

    $d =$ _____, $C =$ _____

10. $d = 15$ in.

    $r =$ _____, $C =$ _____

Find the exact circumference of each circle.

11.

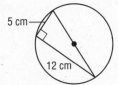
5 cm
12 cm

12.

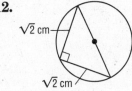
$\sqrt{2}$ cm
$\sqrt{2}$ cm

Lesson 10-1

10-1 Skills Practice

Circles and Circumference

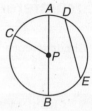

For Exercises 1–5, refer to the circle at the right.

1. Name the circle.

2. Name a radius.

3. Name a chord.

4. Name a diameter.

5. Name a radius not drawn as part of a diameter.

6. Suppose the diameter of the circle is 16 centimeters. Find the radius.

7. If $PC = 11$ inches, find AB.

The diameters of $\odot F$ and $\odot G$ are 5 and 6 units, respectively. Find each measure.

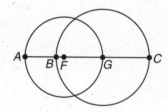

8. BF

9. AB

The radius, diameter, or circumference of a circle is given. Find the missing measures to the nearest hundredth.

10. $r = 8$ cm

   $d = $ _____ , $C \approx$ _____

11. $r = 13$ ft

   $d = $ _____ , $C \approx$ _____

12. $d = 9$ m

   $r = $ _____ , $C \approx$ _____

13. $C = 35.7$ in.

   $d \approx$ _____ , $r \approx$ _____

Find the exact circumference of each circle.

14.

3 cm

15.

8 ft

15 ft

10-1 Practice

Circles and Circumference

For Exercises 1–7, refer to the circle at the right.

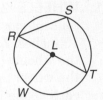

1. Name the circle.

2. Name a radius.

3. Name a chord.

4. Name a diameter.

5. Name a radius not drawn as part of a diameter.

6. Suppose the radius of the circle is 3.5 yards. Find the diameter.

7. If RT = 19 meters, find LW.

The diameters of ⊙L and ⊙M are 20 and 13 units, respectively. Find each measure if QR = 4.

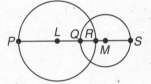

8. LQ

9. RM

The radius, diameter, or circumference of a circle is given. Find the missing measures to the nearest hundredth.

10. r = 7.5 mm

$d =$ _____, $C ≈$ _____

11. C = 227.6 yd

$d ≈$ _____, $r ≈$ _____

Find the exact circumference of each circle.

12.

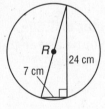

13.

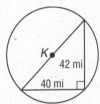

SUNDIALS For Exercises 14 and 15, use the following information.

Herman purchased a sundial to use as the centerpiece for a garden. The diameter of the sundial is 9.5 inches.

14. Find the radius of the sundial.

15. Find the circumference of the sundial to the nearest hundredth.

10-1 Word Problem Practice

Circles and Circumference

1. **WHEELS** Zack is designing wheels for a concept car. The diameter of the wheel is 18 inches. Zack wants to make spokes in the wheel that run from the center of the wheel to the rim. In other words, each spoke is a radius of the wheel. How long are these spokes?

2. **CAKE CUTTING** Kathy slices through a circular cake. The cake has a diameter of 14 inches. The slice that Kathy made is straight and has a length of 11 inches.

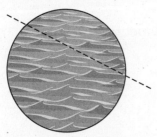

Did Kathy cut along a *radius,* a *diameter,* or a *chord* of the circle?

3. **COINS** Three identical circular coins are lined up in a row as shown.

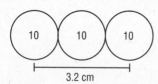

The distance between the centers of the first and third coins is 3.2 centimeters. What is the radius of one of these coins?

4. **PLAZAS** A rectangular plaza has a surrounding circular fence. The diagonals of the rectangle pass from one point on the fence through the center of the circle to another point on the fence.

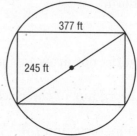

Based on the information in the figure, what is the diameter of the fence? Round your answer to the nearest tenth of a foot.

EXERCISE HOOPS For Exercises 5 and 6, use the following information.
Taiga wants to make a circular loop that he can twirl around his body for exercise. He will use a tube that is 2.5 meters long.

5. What will be the diameter of Taiga's exercise hoop? Round your answer to the nearest thousandth of a meter.

6. What will be the radius of Taiga's exercise hoop? Round your answer to the nearest thousandth of a meter.

10-1 Enrichment

Sectors

The area of a circle is found by using the formula $A = \pi r^2$. A sector is a pie-shaped portion of the circle enclosed by 2 radii and the edge of the circle. A central angle of a sector is an angle whose vertex is at the center of the circle and crosses the circle.

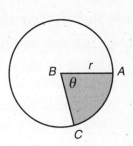

The area of a circle is represented by the formula $A = \pi r^2$. The area of the sector θ is proportional to the part that the central angle is of 360°.

$$\frac{\text{area of sector}}{\text{area of the circle}} = \frac{\theta}{360} \quad \text{or area of sector} = \frac{\theta}{360}\pi r^2.$$

Example   Find the area of the sector shown at the right.

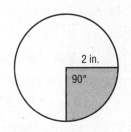

$$A = \frac{\theta}{360}\pi r^2$$

$$A = \frac{90}{360}\pi 2^2 \quad r = 2, \theta = 90$$

$$= \frac{1}{4}(4\pi) \text{ or } \pi$$

So the area of the sector is π in^2 or approximately 3.14 square inches.

Exercises

1. Find the area of a sector if the circle has a radius of 10 centimeters and the central angle measures 72°.

2. Find the area of a sector if the circle has a radius of 5 inches and the central angle measures 60°.

3. If the area of a sector is 15π square centimeters and the radius of the circle is 5 centimeters, find the measure of the central angle.

4. Find the measure of the central angle that intercepts a sector that is $\frac{1}{3}$ the area of the circle.

Lesson 10-1

10-2 Lesson Reading Guide

Measuring Angles and Arcs

Get Ready for the Lesson

Read the introduction to Lesson 10-2 in your textbook.

• What is the measure of the angle formed by the hour hand and the minute hand of the clock at 5:00?

• What is the measure of the angle formed by the hour hand and the minute hand at 10:30? (Hint: How has each hand moved since 10:00?)

Read the Lesson

1. Refer to $\odot P$. $\overline{AC}$ is a diameter. Indicate whether each statement is *true* or *false*.

   a. $\overarc{DAB}$ is a major arc.

   b. $\overarc{ADC}$ is a semicircle.

   c. $\overarc{AD} \cong \overarc{CD}$

   d. $\overarc{DA}$ and $\overarc{AB}$ are adjacent arcs.

   e. $\angle BPC$ is an acute central angle.

   f. $\angle DPA$ and $\angle BPA$ are supplementary central angles.

2. Refer to the figure in Exercise 1. Give each of the following arc measures.

   a. $m\overarc{AB}$ | **b.** $m\overarc{CD}$

   c. $m\overarc{BC}$ | **d.** $m\overarc{ADC}$

   e. $m\overarc{DAB}$ | **f.** $m\overarc{DCB}$

   g. $m\overarc{DAC}$ | **h.** $m\overarc{BDA}$

3. Underline the correct word or number to form a true statement.

   a. The arc measure of a semicircle is (90/180/360).

   b. Arcs of a circle that have exactly one point in common are (congruent/opposite/adjacent) arcs.

   c. The measure of a major arc is greater than (0/90/180) and less than (90/180/360).

   d. Suppose a set of central angles of a circle have interiors that do not overlap. If the angles and their interiors contain all points of the circle, then the sum of the measures of the central angles is (90/270/360).

   e. The measure of an arc formed by two adjacent arcs is the (sum/difference/product) of the measures of the two arcs.

   f. The measure of a minor arc is greater than (0/90/180) and less than (90/180/360).

Remember What You Learned

4. A good way to remember something is to explain it to someone else. Suppose your classmate Luis does not like to work with proportions. What is a way that he can find the length of a minor arc of a circle without solving a proportion?

10-2 Study Guide and Intervention

Measuring Angles and Arcs

Angles and Arcs A **central angle** is an angle whose vertex is at the center of a circle and whose sides are radii. A central angle separates a circle into two arcs, a **major arc** and a **minor arc**.

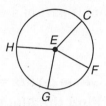

$\overarc{GF}$ is a minor arc.
$\overarc{CHG}$ is a major arc.
$\angle GEF$ is a central angle.

Here are some properties of central angles and arcs.

- The sum of the measures of the central angles of a circle with no interior points in common is 360.

$m\angle HEC + m\angle CEF + m\angle FEG + m\angle GEH = 360$

- The measure of a minor arc equals the measure of its central angle.

$m\overarc{CF} = m\angle CEF$

- The measure of a major arc is 360 minus the measure of the minor arc.

$m\overarc{CGF} = 360 - m\overarc{CF}$

- Two arcs are congruent if and only if their corresponding central angles are congruent.

$\overarc{CF} \cong \overarc{FG}$ if and only if $\angle CEF \cong \angle FEG$.

- The measure of an arc formed by two adjacent arcs is the sum of the measures of the two arcs. **(Arc Addition Postulate)**

$m\overarc{CF} + m\overarc{FG} = m\overarc{CG}$

Example In $\odot R$, $m\angle ARB = 42$ and $\overline{AC}$ is a diameter. Find $m\overarc{AB}$ and $m\overarc{ACB}$.

$\angle ARB$ is a central angle and $m\angle ARB = 42$, so $m\overarc{AB} = 42$.
Thus $m\overarc{ACB} = 360 - 42$ or 318.

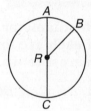

Exercises

Find each measure.

1. $m\angle SCT$

2. $m\angle SCU$

3. $m\angle SCQ$

4. $m\angle QCT$

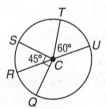

In $\odot O$, $m\angle BOA = 44$. Find each measure.

5. $m\overarc{BA}$

6. $m\overarc{BC}$

7. $m\overarc{CD}$

8. $m\overarc{ACB}$

9. $m\overarc{BCD}$

10. $m\overarc{AD}$

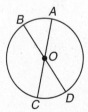

13

Lesson 10-2

10-2 Study Guide and Intervention (continued)

Measuring Angles and Arcs

Arc Length An arc is part of a circle and its length is a part of the circumference of the circle.

Example In $\odot R$, $m\angle ARB = 135$, $RB = 8$, and AC is a diameter. Find the length of $\widehat{AB}$.

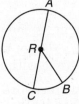

$m\angle ARB = 135$, so $m\widehat{AB} = 135$. Using the formula $C = 2\pi r$, the circumference is $2\pi(8)$ or 16π. To find the length of $\widehat{AB}$, write a proportion to compare each part to its whole.

$\dfrac{\text{length of } \widehat{AB}}{\text{circumference}} = \dfrac{\text{degree measure of arc}}{\text{degree measure of circle}}$ Proportion

$\dfrac{\ell}{16\pi} = \dfrac{135}{360}$ Substitution

$\ell = \dfrac{(16\pi)(135)}{360}$ Multiply each side by 16π.

$= 6\pi$ Simplify.

The length of $\widehat{AB}$ is 6π or about 18.85 units.

Exercises

The diameter of $\odot O$ is 24 units long. Find the length of each arc for the given angle measure. Round to the nearest tenth.

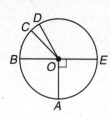

1. $\widehat{DE}$ if $m\angle DOE = 120$

2. $\widehat{DEA}$ if $m\angle DOE = 120$

3. $\widehat{BC}$ if $m\angle COB = 45$

4. $\widehat{CBA}$ if $m\angle COB = 45$

The diameter of $\odot P$ is 15 units long and $\angle SPT \cong \angle RPT$. Find the length of each arc for the given angle measure. Round to the nearest tenth.

5. $\widehat{RT}$ if $m\angle SPT = 70$

6. $\widehat{NR}$ if $m\angle RPT = 50$

7. $\widehat{MST}$

8. $\widehat{MRS}$ if $m\angle MPS = 140$

10-2 Skills Practice

Measuring Angles and Arcs

ALGEBRA In $\odot R$, $\overline{AC}$ and $\overline{EB}$ are diameters. Find each measure.

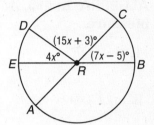

1. $m\angle ERD$

2. $m\angle CRD$

3. $m\angle BRC$

4. $m\angle ARB$

5. $m\angle ARE$

6. $m\angle BRD$

In $\odot A$, $m\angle PAU = 40$, $\angle PAU \cong \angle SAT$, and $\angle RAS \cong \angle TAU$. Find each measure.

7. $m\widehat{PQ}$

8. $m\widehat{PQR}$

9. $m\widehat{ST}$

10. $m\widehat{RS}$

11. $m\widehat{RSU}$

12. $m\widehat{STP}$

13. $m\widehat{PQS}$

14. $m\widehat{PRU}$

The diameter of $\odot D$ is 18 units long. Find the length of each arc for the given angle measure.

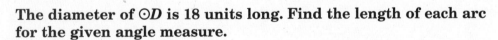

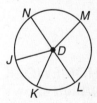

15. $\widehat{LM}$ if $m\angle LDM = 100$

16. $\widehat{MN}$ if $m\angle MDN = 80$

17. $\widehat{KL}$ if $m\angle KDL = 60$

18. $\widehat{NJK}$ if $m\angle NDK = 120$

19. $\widehat{KLM}$ if $m\angle KDM = 160$

20. $\widehat{JK}$ if $m\angle JDK = 50$

Lesson 10-2

10-2 Practice

Measuring Angles and Arcs

ALGEBRA In ⊙Q, $\overline{AC}$ and $\overline{BD}$ are diameters. Find each measure.

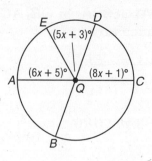

1. $m\angle AQE$ **2.** $m\angle DQE$

3. $m\angle CQD$ **4.** $m\angle BQC$

5. $m\angle CQE$ **6.** $m\angle AQD$

In ⊙P, $m\angle GPH = 38$. Find each measure.

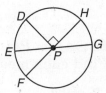

7. $m\widehat{EF}$ **8.** $m\widehat{DE}$

9. $m\widehat{FG}$ **10.** $m\widehat{DHG}$

11. $m\widehat{DFG}$ **12.** $m\widehat{DGE}$

The radius of ⊙Z is 13.5 units long. Find the length of each arc for the given angle measure.

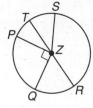

13. $\widehat{QPT}$ if $m\angle QZT = 120$ **14.** $\widehat{QR}$ if $m\angle QZR = 60$

15. $\widehat{PQR}$ if $m\angle PZR = 150$ **16.** $\widehat{QPS}$ if $m\angle QZS = 160$

HOMEWORK For Exercises 17 and 18, refer to the table, which shows the number of hours students at Leland High School say they spend on homework each night.

17. If you were to construct a circle graph of the data, how many degrees would be allotted to each category?

Homework	
Less than 1 hour	8%
1–2 hours	29%
2–3 hours	58%
3–4 hours	3%
Over 4 hours	2%

18. Describe the arcs associated with each category.

10-2 Word Problem Practice

Measuring Angles and Arcs

1. **CONDIMENTS** A number of people in a park were asked to name their favorite condiment for hot dogs. The results are shown in the circle graph.

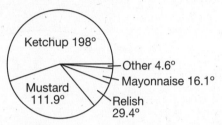

Ketchup 198°
Other 4.6°
Mayonnaise 16.1°
Mustard 111.9°
Relish 29.4°

What was the second most popular hot dog condiment?

2. **CLOCKS** Shiatsu is a Japanese massage technique. One of the beliefs is that various body functions are most active at various times during the day. To illustrate this, they use a Chinese clock that is based on a circle divided into 12 equal sections by radii.

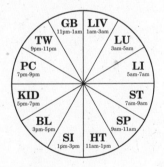

What is the measure of any one of the 12 equal central angles?

3. **PIES** Yolanda has divided a circular apple pie into 4 slices by cutting the pie along 4 radii. The central angles of the 4 slices are $3x$, $6x - 10$, $4x + 10$, and $5x$ degrees. What exactly are the numerical measures of the central angles?

4. **RIBBONS** Cora is wrapping a ribbon around a cylinder-shaped gift box. The box has a diameter of 15 inches and the ribbon is 60 inches long. Cora is able to wrap the ribbon all the way around the box once, and then continue so that the second end of the ribbon passes the first end. What is the central angle formed between the ends of the ribbon? Round your answer to the nearest tenth of a degree.

BIKE WHEELS For Exercises 5–7, use the following information.

Lucy had to buy a new wheel for her bike. The bike wheel has a diameter of 20 inches.

5. If Lucy rolls the wheel one complete rotation along the ground, how far will the wheel travel? Round your answer to the nearest hundredth of an inch.

6. If the bike wheel is rolled along the ground so that it rotates 45°, how far will the wheel travel? Round your answer to the nearest hundredth of an inch.

7. If the bike wheel is rolled along the ground for 10 inches, through what angle does the wheel rotate? Round your answer to the nearest tenth of a degree.

Lesson 10-2

10-2 Enrichment

Curves of Constant Width

A circle is called a curve of constant width because no matter how you turn it, the greatest distance across it is always the same. However, the circle is not the only figure with this property.

The figure at the right is called a Reuleaux triangle.

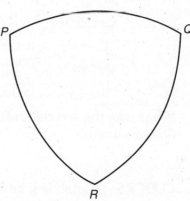

1. Use a metric ruler to find the distance from *P* to any point on the opposite side.

2. Find the distance from *Q* to the opposite side.

3. What is the distance from *R* to the opposite side?

The Reuleaux triangle is made of three arcs. In the example shown, $\overset{\frown}{PQ}$ has center *R*, $\overset{\frown}{QR}$ has center *P*, and $\overset{\frown}{PR}$ has center *Q*.

4. Trace the Reuleaux triangle above on a piece of paper and cut it out. Make a square with sides the length you found in Exercise 1. Show that you can turn the triangle inside the square while keeping its sides in contact with the sides of the square.

5. Make a different curve of constant width by starting with the five points below and following the steps given.

   Step 1: Place the point of your compass on *D* with opening *DA*. Make an arc with endpoints *A* and *B*.

   Step 2: Make another arc from *B* to *C* that has center *E*.

   Step 3: Continue this process until you have five arcs drawn.

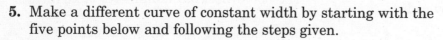

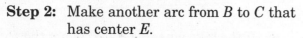

Some countries use shapes like this for coins. They are useful because they can be distinguished by touch, yet they will work in vending machines because of their constant width.

6. Measure the width of the figure you made in Exercise 5. Draw two parallel lines with the distance between them equal to the width you found. On a piece of paper, trace the five-sided figure and cut it out. Show that it will roll between the lines drawn.

10-3 Lesson Reading Guide

Arcs and Chords

Get Ready for the Lesson

Read the introduction to Lesson 10-3 in your textbook.

What do you observe about any two of the grooves in the waffle iron shown in the picture in your textbook?

Read the Lesson

1. Supply the missing words or phrases to form true statements.

   a. In a circle, if a radius is _____ to a chord, then it bisects the chord and its _____.

   b. In a circle or in _____ circles, two _____ are congruent if and only if their corresponding chords are congruent.

   c. In a circle or in _____ circles, two chords are congruent if they are _____ from the center.

   d. A polygon is inscribed in a circle if all of its _____ lie on the circle.

   e. All of the sides of an inscribed polygon are _____ of the circle.

2. If ⊙P has a diameter 40 centimeters long, and $AC = FD = 24$ centimeters, find each measure.

   a. PA   **b.** AG

   c. PE   **d.** PH

   e. HE   **f.** FG

   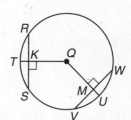

3. In ⊙Q, $RS = VW$ and $m\widehat{RS} = 70$. Find each measure.

   a. $m\widehat{RT}$ **b.** $m\widehat{ST}$

   c. $m\widehat{VW}$ **d.** $m\widehat{VU}$

4. Find the measure of each arc of a circle that is circumscribed about the polygon.

   a. an equilateral triangle   **b.** a regular pentagon

   c. a regular hexagon   **d.** a regular decagon

   e. a regular dodecagon   **f.** a regular n-gon

Remember What You Learned

5. Some students have trouble distinguishing between *inscribed* and *circumscribed* figures. What is an easy way to remember which is which?

Lesson 10-3

10-3 Study Guide and Intervention (continued)

Arcs and Chords

Arcs and Chords Points on a circle determine both chords and arcs. Several properties are related to points on a circle.

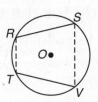

- In a circle or in congruent circles, two minor arcs are congruent if and only if their corresponding chords are congruent.
- If all the vertices of a polygon lie on a circle, the polygon is said to be **inscribed** in the circle and the circle is **circumscribed** about the polygon.

$\overset{\frown}{RS} \cong \overset{\frown}{TV}$ if and only if $\overline{RS} \cong \overline{TV}$.
RSVT is inscribed in $\odot O$.
$\odot O$ is circumscribed about *RSVT*.

Example Trapezoid *ABCD* is inscribed in $\odot O$.
If $\overline{AB} \cong \overline{BC} \cong \overline{CD}$ and $m\overset{\frown}{BC} = 50$, what is $m\overset{\frown}{APD}$?
Chords $\overline{AB}$, $\overline{BC}$, and $\overline{CD}$ are congruent, so $\overset{\frown}{AB}$, $\overset{\frown}{BC}$, and $\overset{\frown}{CD}$ are congruent. $m\overset{\frown}{BC} = 50$, so $m\overset{\frown}{AB} + m\overset{\frown}{BC} + m\overset{\frown}{CD} = 50 + 50 + 50 = 150$. Then $m\overset{\frown}{APD} = 360 - 150$ or 210.

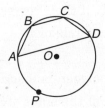

Exercises

Each regular polygon is inscribed in a circle. Determine the measure of each arc that corresponds to a side of the polygon.

1. hexagon

2. pentagon

3. triangle

4. square

5. octagon

6. 36-gon

Determine the measure of each arc of the circle circumscribed about the polygon.

7.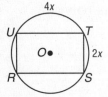

8.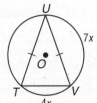

9.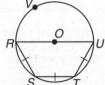

10-3 Study Guide and Intervention *(continued)*

Arcs and Chords

Diameters and Chords

- In a circle, if a diameter is perpendicular to a chord, then it bisects the chord and its arc.
- In a circle or in congruent circles, two chords are congruent if and only if they are equidistant from the center.

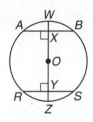

If $\overline{WZ} \perp \overline{AB}$, then $\overline{AX} \cong \overline{XB}$ and $\overarc{AW} \cong \overarc{WB}$.

If $OX = OY$, then $\overline{AB} \cong \overline{RS}$.

If $\overline{AB} \cong \overline{RS}$, then $\overline{AB}$ and $\overline{RS}$ are equidistant from point O.

Example In $\odot O$, $\overline{CD} \perp \overline{OE}$, $OD = 15$, and $CD = 24$. Find x.

A diameter or radius perpendicular to a chord bisects the chord, so ED is half of CD.

$ED = \frac{1}{2}(24)$

$\quad\; = 12$

Use the Pythagorean Theorem to find x in $\triangle OED$.

$(OE)^2 + (ED)^2 = (OD)^2$ Pythagorean Theorem

$\quad\;\; x^2 + 12^2 = 15^2$ Substitution

$\quad\;\; x^2 + 144 = 225$ Multiply.

$\qquad\qquad x^2 = 81$ Subtract 144 from each side.

$\qquad\qquad\; x = 9$ Take the square root of each side.

Exercises

In $\odot P$, $CD = 24$ and $m\overarc{CY} = 45$. Find each measure.

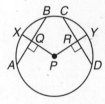

1. AQ

2. RC

3. QB

4. AB

5. $m\overarc{DY}$

6. $m\overarc{AB}$

7. $m\overarc{AX}$

8. $m\overarc{XB}$

9. $m\overarc{CD}$

In $\odot G$, $DG = GU$ and $AC = RT$. Find each measure.

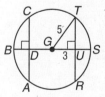

10. TU

11. TR

12. $m\overarc{TS}$

13. CD

14. GD

15. $m\overarc{AB}$

16. A chord of a circle 20 inches long is 24 inches from the center of a circle. Find the length of the radius.

Lesson 10-3

10-3 Skills Practice

Arcs and Chords

In ⊙H, $m\overarc{RS} = 82$, $m\overarc{TU} = 82$, $RS = 46$, and $\overline{TU} \cong \overline{RS}$.
Find each measure.

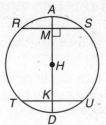

1. TU

2. TK

3. MS

4. $m\angle HKU$

5. $m\overarc{AS}$

6. $m\overarc{AR}$

7. $m\overarc{TD}$

8. $m\overarc{DU}$

The radius of ⊙Y is 34, $AB = 60$, and $m\overarc{AC} = 71$. Find each measure.

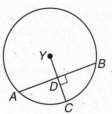

9. $m\overarc{BC}$

10. $m\overarc{AB}$

11. AD

12. BD

13. YD

14. DC

In ⊙X, $LX = MX$, $XY = 58$, and $VW = 84$. Find each measure.

15. YZ

16. YM

17. MX

18. MZ

19. LV

20. LX

10-3 Practice

Arcs and Chords

In $\odot E$, $m\widehat{HQ} = 48$, $HI = JK$, and $JR = 7.5$. Find each measure.

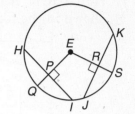

1. $m\widehat{HI}$ 2. $m\widehat{QI}$

3. $m\widehat{JK}$ 4. HI

5. PI 6. JK

The radius of $\odot N$ is 18, $NK = 9$, and $m\widehat{DE} = 120$. Find each measure.

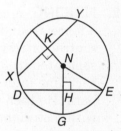

7. $m\widehat{GE}$ 8. $m\angle HNE$

9. $m\angle HEN$ 10. HN

The radius of $\odot O = 32$, $\widehat{PQ} \cong \widehat{RS}$, and $PQ = 56$. Find each measure.

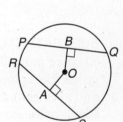

11. PB 14. BQ

12. OB 16. RS

13. **MANDALAS** The base figure in a mandala design is a nine-pointed star. Find the measure of each arc of the circle circumscribed about the star.

Lesson 10-3

10-3 Word Problem Practice

Arcs and Chords

1. HEXAGON A hexagon is constructed as shown in the figure.

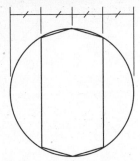

How many different chord lengths occur as side lengths of the hexagon?

2. FENCING A contractor is hired to build a fence around a circular park. The contractor traces out 10 radial lines each separated by 36°. He places a post where each line intersects the perimeter of the park. He then connects consecutive posts with a straight fence. The result is a fence that has the shape of a polygon with 10 sides. Is this polygon a regular decagon? Explain.

3. BIKE PATHS Carl is planning to visit a circular park. The radius of the park is 8 miles. He is looking at a map of the park and sees that the park has five landmarks along its edge. The landmarks are connected by paths of equal length for biking. These paths form a regular pentagon inscribed in the circle. If Carl bikes along these paths to visit each landmark, how many miles will he bike?

4. CENTERS Neil wants to find the center of a large circle drawn in the pavement of the schoolyard. He draws what he thinks is a diameter of the circle and then marks its midpoint and declares that he has found the center. His teacher comes by and asks Neil how he knows that the line he drew is really the diameter of the circle and not a smaller chord. Neil realizes that he does not know for sure. Explain what Neil can do to determine if it is an actual diameter.

A TALE OF TWO TRIANGLES For Exercises 5 and 6, use the following information.

An equilateral triangle is inscribed in a circle with center O. The triangle is then rotated 30° to obtain another equilateral triangle inscribed in the circle.

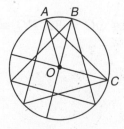

5. What is $m\angle AOC$?

6. Prove that the diameter through B is perpendicular to the diameter through C.

10-3 Enrichment

Patterns from Chords

Some beautiful and interesting patterns result if you draw chords to connect evenly spaced points on a circle. On the circle shown below, 24 points have been marked to divide the circle into 24 equal parts. Numbers from 1 to 48 have been placed beside the points. Study the diagram to see exactly how this was done.

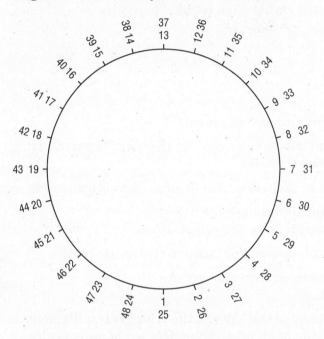

1. Use your ruler and pencil to draw chords to connect numbered points as follows: 1 to 2, 2 to 4, 3 to 6, 4 to 8, and so on. Keep doubling until you have gone all the way around the circle. What kind of pattern do you get?

2. Copy the original circle, points, and numbers. Try other patterns for connecting points. For example, you might try tripling the first number to get the number for the second endpoint of each chord. Keep special patterns for a possible class display.

Lesson 10-3

10-4 Lesson Reading Guide

Inscribed Angles

Get Ready for the Lesson

Read the introduction to Lesson 10-4 in your textbook.

*   Why do you think regular hexagons are used rather than squares for the "hole" in a socket?

*   Why do you think regular hexagons are used rather than regular polygons with more sides?

Read the Lesson

1. Underline the correct word or phrase to form a true statement.

   a. An angle whose vertex is on a circle and whose sides contain chords of the circle is called a(n) (central/inscribed/circumscribed) angle.

   b. Every inscribed angle that intercepts a semicircle is a(n) (acute/right/obtuse) angle.

   c. The opposite angles of an inscribed quadrilateral are (congruent/complementary/supplementary).

   d. An inscribed angle that intercepts a major arc is a(n) (acute/right/obtuse) angle.

   e. Two inscribed angles of a circle that intercept the same arc are (congruent/complementary/supplementary).

   f. If a triangle is inscribed in a circle and one of the sides of the triangle is a diameter of the circle, the diameter is (the longest side of an acute triangle/a leg of an isosceles triangle/the hypotenuse of a right triangle).

2. Refer to the figure. Find each measure.

   a. $m\angle ABC$ **b.** $m\widehat{CD}$

   c. $m\widehat{AD}$ **d.** $m\angle BAC$

   e. $m\angle BCA$ **f.** $m\widehat{AB}$

   g. $m\widehat{BCD}$ **h.** $m\widehat{BDA}$

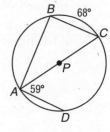

Remember What You Learned

3. A good way to remember a geometric relationship is to visualize it. Describe how you could make a sketch that would help you remember the relationship between the measure of an inscribed angle and the measure of its intercepted arc.

10-4 Study Guide and Intervention

Inscribed Angles

Inscribed Angles An **inscribed angle** is an angle whose vertex is on a circle and whose sides contain chords of the circle. In $\odot G$, inscribed $\angle DEF$ intercepts $\widehat{DF}$.

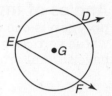

$m\angle DEF = \frac{1}{2}m\widehat{DF}$

Inscribed Angle Theorem	If an angle is inscribed in a circle, then the measure of the angle equals one-half the measure of its intercepted arc.

Example   In $\odot G$ above, $m\widehat{DF} = 90$. Find $m\angle DEF$.

$\angle DEF$ is an inscribed angle so its measure is half of the intercepted arc.

$m\angle DEF = \frac{1}{2}m\widehat{DF}$

$\qquad\quad = \frac{1}{2}(90)$ or 45

Exercises

Use $\odot P$ for Exercises 1–10. In $\odot P$, $\overline{RS} \parallel \overline{TV}$ and $\overline{RT} \cong \overline{SV}$.

1. Name the intercepted arc for $\angle RTS$.

2. Name an inscribed angle that intercepts $\widehat{SV}$.

In $\odot P$, $m\widehat{SV} = 120$ and $m\angle RPS = 76$. Find each measure.

3. $m\angle PRS$

4. $m\widehat{RSV}$

5. $m\widehat{RT}$

6. $m\angle RVT$

7. $m\angle QRS$

8. $m\angle STV$

9. $m\widehat{TV}$

10. $m\angle SVT$

Lesson 10-4

10-4 Study Guide and Intervention (continued)

Inscribed Angles

Angles of Inscribed Polygons An **inscribed polygon** is one whose sides are chords of a circle and whose vertices are points on the circle. Inscribed polygons have several properties.

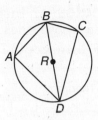

- If an angle of an inscribed polygon intercepts a semicircle, the angle is a right angle.

  If $\overset{\frown}{BCD}$ is a semicircle, then $m\angle BCD = 90$.

- If a quadrilateral is inscribed in a circle, then its opposite angles are supplementary.

  For inscribed quadrilateral $ABCD$,
  $m\angle A + m\angle C = 180$ and
  $m\angle ABC + m\angle ADC = 180$.

Example In ⊙R above, $BC = 3$ and $BD = 5$. Find each measure.

a. $m\angle C$

$\angle C$ intercepts a semicircle. Therefore $\angle C$ is a right angle and $m\angle C = 90$.

b. CD

$\triangle BCD$ is a right triangle, so use the Pythagorean Theorem to find CD.

$$(CD)^2 + (BC)^2 = (BD)^2$$
$$(CD)^2 + 3^2 = 5^2$$
$$(CD)^2 = 25 - 9$$
$$(CD)^2 = 16$$
$$CD = 4$$

Exercises

Find the measure of each angle or segment for each figure.

1. $m\angle X, m\angle Y$

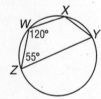

2. AD

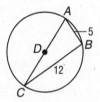

3. $m\angle 1, m\angle 2$

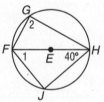

4. $m\angle 1, m\angle 2$

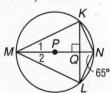

5. AB, AC

6. $m\angle 1, m\angle 2$

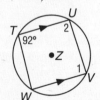

10-4 Skills Practice

Inscribed Angles

In $\odot S$, $m\widehat{KL} = 80$, $m\widehat{LM} = 100$, and $m\widehat{MN} = 60$. Find the measure of each angle.

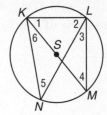

1. $m\angle 1$ **2.** $m\angle 2$

3. $m\angle 3$ **4.** $m\angle 4$

5. $m\angle 5$ **6.** $m\angle 6$

ALGEBRA Find the measure of each numbered angle for each figure.

7. $m\angle 1 = 5x - 2$, $m\angle 2 = 2x + 8$ **8.** $m\angle 1 = 5x$, $m\angle 3 = 3x + 10$,
                                                         $m\angle 4 = y + 7$, $m\angle 6 = 3y + 11$

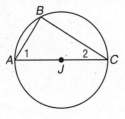   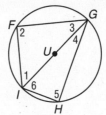

Quadrilateral $RSTU$ is inscribed in $\odot P$ such that $m\widehat{STU} = 220$ and $m\angle S = 95$. Find each measure.

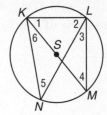

9. $m\angle R$ **10.** $m\angle T$

11. $m\angle U$ **12.** $m\widehat{SRU}$

13. $m\widehat{RUT}$ **14.** $m\widehat{RST}$

Lesson 10-4

10-4 Practice

Inscribed Angles

In ⊙B, $m\widehat{WX} = 104$, $m\widehat{WZ} = 88$, and $m\angle ZWY = 26$. Find the measure of each angle.

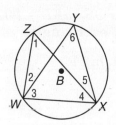

1. $m\angle 1$

2. $m\angle 2$

3. $m\angle 3$

4. $m\angle 4$

5. $m\angle 5$

6. $m\angle 6$

ALGEBRA Find the measure of each numbered angle for each figure.

7. $m\angle 1 = 5x + 2$, $m\angle 2 = 2x - 3$
$m\angle 3 = 7y - 1$, $m\angle 4 = 2y + 10$

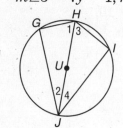

8. $m\angle 1 = 4x - 7$, $m\angle 2 = 2x + 11$,
$m\angle 3 = 5y - 14$, $m\angle 4 = 3y + 8$

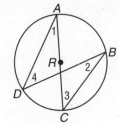

Quadrilateral *EFGH* is inscribed in ⊙N such that $m\widehat{FG} = 97$, $m\widehat{GH} = 117$, and $m\widehat{EHG} = 164$. Find each measure.

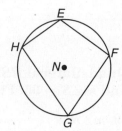

9. $m\angle E$

10. $m\angle F$

11. $m\angle G$

12. $m\angle H$

13. PROBABILITY In ⊙V, point *C* is randomly located so that it does not coincide with points *R* or *S*. If $m\widehat{RS} = 140$, what is the probability that $m\angle RCS = 70$?

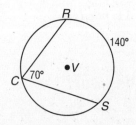

10-4 **Word Problem Practice**
Inscribed Angles

1. **ARENA** A circus arena is lit by five lights equally spaced around the perimeter.

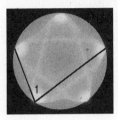

What is $m\angle 1$?

2. **FIELD OF VIEW** The figure shows a top view of two people in front of a very tall rectangular wall. The wall makes a chord of a circle that passes through both people.

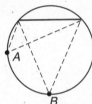

Which person has more of their horizontal field of vision blocked by the wall?

3. **RHOMBI** Paul is interested in circumscribing a circle around a rhombus that is not a square. He is having great difficulty doing so. Can you help him? Explain.

4. **STREETS** Three kilometers separate the intersections of Cross and Upton and Cross and Hope.

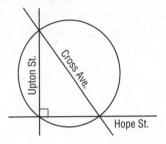

What is the distance between the intersection of Upton and Hope and the point midway between the intersections of Upton and Cross and Cross and Hope?

INSCRIBED HEXAGONS For Exercises 5 and 6, use the following information.

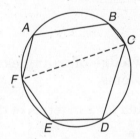

You will prove that the sum of the measures of alternate interior angles in an inscribed hexagon is 360.

5. How are $\angle A$ and $\angle BCF$ related? Similarly, how are $\angle E$ and $\angle DCF$ related?

6. Show that $m\angle A + m\angle BCD + m\angle E = 360°$.

Lesson 10-4

10-4 Enrichment

Formulas for Regular Polygons

Suppose a regular polygon of n sides is inscribed in a circle of radius r. The figure shows one of the isosceles triangles formed by joining the endpoints of one side of the polygon to the center C of the circle. In the figure, s is the length of each side of the regular polygon, and a is the length of the segment from C perpendicular to $\overline{AB}$.

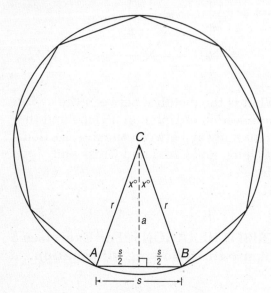

Use your knowledge of triangles and trigonometry to solve the following problems.

1. Find a formula for x in terms of the number of sides n of the polygon.

2. Find a formula for s in terms of the number of n and r. Use trigonometry.

3. Find a formula for a in terms of n and r. Use trigonometry.

4. Find a formula for the *perimeter* of the regular polygon in terms of n and r.

10-5 Lesson Reading Guide

Tangents

Get Ready for the Lesson

Read the introduction to Lesson 10-5 in your textbook.

How is the hammer throw event related to the mathematical concept of a tangent line?

Read the Lesson

1. Refer to the figure. Name each of the following.

   a. two lines that are tangent to ⊙*P*

   b. two points of tangency

   c. two chords of the circle

   d. three radii of the circle

   e. two right angles

   f. two congruent right triangles

   g. the hypotenuse or hypotenuses in the two congruent right triangles

   h. two congruent central angles

   i. two congruent minor arcs

   j. an inscribed angle

2. Explain the difference between an *inscribed polygon* and a *circumscribed polygon*. Use the words *vertex* and *tangent* in your explanation.

Remember What You Learned

3. A good way to remember a mathematical term is to relate it to a word or expression that is used in a nonmathematical way. Sometimes a word or expression used in English is derived from a mathematical term. What does it mean to "go off on a tangent," and how is this meaning related to the geometric idea of a *tangent* line?

Lesson 10-5

10-5 Study Guide and Intervention *(continued)*

Tangents

Tangents A tangent to a circle intersects the circle in exactly one point, called the **point of tangency**. There are three important relationships involving tangents.

- If a line is tangent to a circle, then it is perpendicular to the radius drawn to the point of tangency.

- If a line is perpendicular to a radius of a circle at its endpoint on the circle, then the line is a tangent to the circle.

- If two segments from the same exterior point are tangent to a circle, then they are congruent.

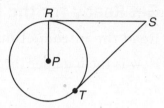

$\overline{RP} \perp \overline{SR}$ if and only if $\overline{SR}$ is tangent to $\odot P$.

If $\overline{SR}$ and $\overline{ST}$ are tangent to $\odot P$, then $\overline{SR} \cong \overline{ST}$.

Example $\overline{AB}$ **is tangent to $\odot C$. Find x.**

$\overline{AB}$ is tangent to $\odot C$, so $\overline{AB}$ is perpendicular to radius $\overline{BC}$. $\overline{CD}$ is a radius, so $CD = 8$ and $AC = 9 + 8$ or 17. Use the Pythagorean Theorem with right $\triangle ABC$.

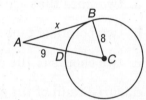

$(AB)^2 + (BC)^2 = (AC)^2$ Pythagorean Theorem

$x^2 + 8^2 = 17^2$ Substitution

$x^2 + 64 = 289$ Multiply.

$x^2 = 225$ Subtract 64 from each side.

$x = 15$ Take the positive square root of each side.

Exercises

Find x. Assume that segments that appear to be tangent are tangent.

1.

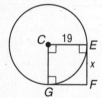

2.

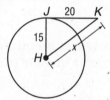

3.

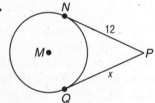

4.

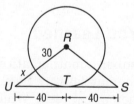

5.

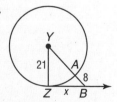

6.

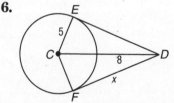

10-5 Study Guide and Intervention (continued)

Tangents

Circumscribed Polygons When a polygon is circumscribed about a circle, all of the sides of the polygon are tangent to the circle.

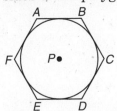

Hexagon *ABCDEF* is circumscribed about ⊙*P*.
$\overline{AB}$, $\overline{BC}$, $\overline{CD}$, $\overline{DE}$, $\overline{EF}$, and $\overline{FA}$ are tangent to ⊙*P*.

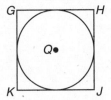

Square *GHJK* is circumscribed about ⊙*Q*.
$\overline{GH}$, $\overline{JH}$, $\overline{JK}$, and $\overline{KG}$ are tangent to ⊙*Q*.

Example △*ABC* is circumscribed about ⊙*O*.
Find the perimeter of △*ABC*.

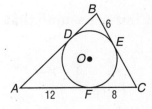

△*ABC* is circumscribed about ⊙*O*, so points *D*, *E*, and *F* are points of tangency. Therefore $AD = AF$, $BE = BD$, and $CF = CE$.

$$P = AD + AF + BE + BD + CF + CE$$
$$= 12 + 12 + 6 + 6 + 8 + 8$$
$$= 52$$

The perimeter is 52 units.

Exercises

Find *x*. Assume that segments that appear to be tangent are tangent.

1.

square

2.

regular hexagon

3.

square

4.

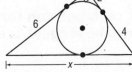

5.

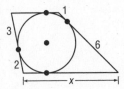

6.

equilateral triangle

Lesson 10-5

10-5 **Skills Practice**

Tangents

Determine whether each segment is tangent to the given circle.

1. $\overline{HI}$

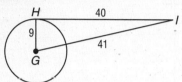

2. $\overline{AB}$

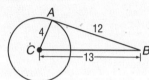

Find *x*. Assume that segments that appear to be tangent are tangent.

3.

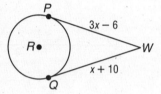

4.

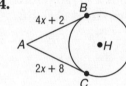

5.

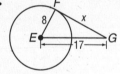

6.

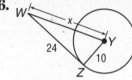

Find the perimeter of each polygon for the given information. Assume that segments that appear to be tangent are tangent.

7. $QT = 4$, $PT = 9$, $SR = 13$

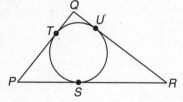

8. $HIJK$ is a rhombus, $SI = 5$, $HR = 13$

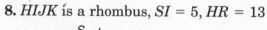
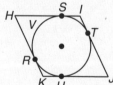

10-5 Practice

Tangents

Determine whether each segment is tangent to the given circle.

1. $\overline{MP}$

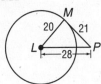

2. $\overline{QR}$

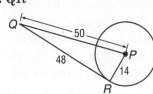

Find x. Assume that segments that appear to be tangent are tangent.

3.

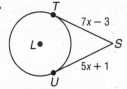

4.

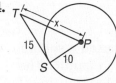

Find the perimeter of each polygon for the given information. Assume that segments that appear to be tangent are tangent.

5. $CD = 52$, $CU = 18$, $TB = 12$

6. $KG = 32$, $HG = 56$

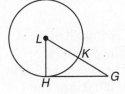

CLOCKS For Exercises 7 and 8, use the following information.

The design shown in the figure is that of a circular clock face inscribed in a triangular base. AF and FC are equal.

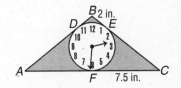

7. Find AB.

8. Find the perimeter of the clock.

Lesson 10-5

10-5 **Word Problem Practice**

Tangents

1. CANALS The concrete canal in Landtown is shaped like a "V" at the bottom. One day, Maureen accidentally dropped a cylindrical tube as she was walking and it rolled to the bottom of the dried out concrete canal. The figure shows a cross section of the tube at the bottom of the canal.

Compare the lengths *AV* and *BV*.

2. PACKAGING Taylor packed a sphere inside a cubic box. He had painted the sides of the box black before putting the sphere inside. When the sphere was later removed, he discovered that the black paint had not completely dried and there were black marks on the sides of the sphere at the points of tangency with the sides of the box. If the black marks are used as the vertices of a polygon, what kind of polygon results?

3. TRIANGLES A circle is inscribed in a 40°-60°-80° triangle. The points of tangency form the vertices of a triangle inscribed in the circle. What are the angles of the inscribed triangle?

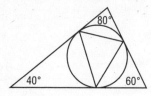

4. ROLLING A wheel is rolling down an incline. Twelve evenly spaced diameters form spokes of the wheel.

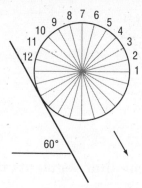

When spoke 2 is vertical, which spoke will be perpendicular to the incline?

DESIGN For Exercises 5 and 6, use the following information.
Amanda wants to make this design of circles inside an equilateral triangle.

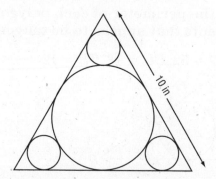

5. What is the radius of the large circle to the nearest hundredth of an inch?

6. What are the radii of the smaller circles to the nearest hundredth of an inch?

10-5 Enrichment

Tangent Circles

Two circles in the same plane are **tangent circles** if they have exactly one point in common. Tangent circles with no common interior points are **externally tangent**. If tangent circles have common interior points, then they are **internally tangent**. Three or more circles are **mutually tangent** if each pair of them is tangent.

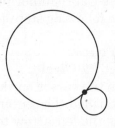

Externally Tangent Circles

Internally Tangent Circles

1. Make sketches to show all possible positions of three mutually tangent circles.

2. Make sketches to show all possible positions of four mutually tangent circles.

3. Make sketches to show all possible positions of five mutually tangent circles.

4. Write a conjecture about the number of possible positions for n mutually tangent circles if n is a whole number greater than four.

Lesson 10-5

10-5 Graphing Calculator Activity

Cabri Junior: Exploring Tangents

A line that intersects a circle in exactly one point is called a **tangent** to the circle. You can use Cabri Junior to explore some of the characteristics of tangents. Use the following steps to draw two lines that are tangent to a circle.

Step 1 Draw a circle.
- Select **F2 Circle.**
- Place the cursor on the left center part of the screen and press ENTER . You have established the center of the circle.
- Press the left arrow to increase the radius length of the circle. Press ENTER when the circle has a desirable radius.
- Select **F5 Alph-num** to label the center of the circle *C*.

Step 2 Place a point outside the circle.
- Select **F2 Point, Point.**
- Move the cursor outside the circle. Press ENTER to establish the point.
- Label the point *A*.

Step 3 Draw a tangent line.
- Select **F2 Line.**
- Draw a line through point *A* that intersects circle *C* in exactly one point.
- Label the point *T*.

Step 4 Draw a second tangent line.
- Repeat the procedure in Step 3 to draw another line through *A* that is tangent to circle *C*.
- Label the point *S*.

The lines drawn to the circle are tangents to the circle. *Note that these tangents are approximate, since it is difficult to find the exact point where the line touches the circle.*

Exercises

Use the measuring capabilities of Cabri Jr. to explore the characteristics of tangents.

1. Measure $\overline{AT}$ and $\overline{AS}$.

2. Move point *A* closer to the circle. (Press CLEAR so the pointer becomes a black arrow. Move the pointer close to point *A* until the arrow becomes transparent and point *A* is blinking. Press ALPHA to change the arrow to a hand. Then move the point.) Adjust $\overline{AT}$ and $\overline{AS}$ accordingly. Make a conjecture about the measurements of $\overline{AT}$ and $\overline{AS}$.

3. Use the Segment tool to draw radii $\overline{CT}$ and $\overline{CS}$. Measure $\angle CTA$ and $\angle CSA$.

4. Make a conjecture about the angles formed by a radius and a tangent to a circle.

10-5 Geometer's Sketchpad Activity

Exploring Tangents

A line that intersects a circle in exactly one point is called a **tangent** to the circle. You can use The Geometer's Sketchpad to explore some of the characteristics of tangents. Use the following steps to draw two lines that are tangent to a circle.

Step 1: Use the Compass tool to draw a circle. Choose the Compass tool in the Tool Box. Then move the pointer to the sketch plane, where it becomes a circle. Position the pointer anywhere on the sketch plane to locate the center of the circle. Then click and drag the pointer until the circle has the desired radius. Release the mouse button to complete the circle. Label the center of the circle C.

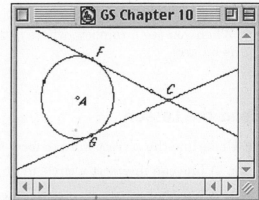

Step 2: Next, use the Point tool to draw a point outside the circle. Label the point A.

Step 3: Use the Line tool to draw a line through point A that intersects circle C in exactly one point. Label the point of intersection T.

Step 4: Repeat the procedure in Step 3 to draw another line through point A that is tangent to circle C at point S.

The lines drawn to the circle are tangents to the circle. *Note that these tangents are approximate, since it is difficult to find the exact point where the line touches the circle.*

> ### Exercises

Use the measuring capabilities of The Geometer's Sketchpad to explore the characteristics of tangents.

1. Measure $\overline{AT}$ and $\overline{AS}$.

2. Move point A closer to the circle. Adjust $\overline{AT}$ and $\overline{AS}$ accordingly. Make a conjecture about the measurements of $\overline{AT}$ and $\overline{AS}$.

3. Use the Segment tool to draw radii $\overline{CT}$ and $\overline{CS}$. Measure $\angle CTA$ and $\angle CSA$.

4. Make a conjecture about the angles formed by a radius and a tangent to a circle.

Lesson 10-5

10-6 Lesson Reading Guide

Secants, Tangents, and Angle Measures

Get Ready for the Lesson

Read the introduction to Lesson 10-6 in your textbook.

- How would you describe ∠C in the figure in your textbook?

- When you see a rainbow, where is the sun in relation to the circle of which the rainbow is an arc?

Read the Lesson

1. Underline the correct word to form a true statement.

   a. A line can intersect a circle in at most (one/two/three) points.

   b. A line that intersects a circle in exactly two points is called a (tangent/secant/radius).

   c. A line that intersects a circle in exactly one point is called a (tangent/secant/radius).

   d. Every secant of a circle contains a (radius/tangent/chord).

2. Determine whether each statement is *always*, *sometimes*, or *never* true.

   a. A secant of a circle passes through the center of the circle.

   b. A tangent to a circle passes through the center of the circle.

   c. A secant-secant angle is a central angle of the circle.

   d. A vertex of a secant-tangent angle is a point on the circle.

   e. A secant-tangent angle passes through the center of the circle.

   f. The vertex of a tangent-tangent angle is a point on the circle.

   g. If one side of a secant-tangent angle passes through the center of the circle, the angle is a right angle.

   h. The measure of a secant-secant angle is one-half the positive difference of the measures of its intercepted arcs.

   i. The sum of the measures of the arcs intercepted by a tangent-tangent angle is 360.

   j. The two arcs intercepted by a tangent-tangent angle are congruent.

Remember What You Learned

3. Some students have trouble remembering the difference between a *secant* and a *tangent*. What is an easy way to remember which is which?

10-6 Study Guide and Intervention

Secants, Tangents, and Angle Measures

Intersections On or Inside a Circle A line that intersects a circle in exactly two points is called a **secant**. The measures of angles formed by secants and tangents are related to intercepted arcs.

- If two secants intersect in the interior of a circle, then the measure of the angle formed is one-half the sum of the measure of the arcs intercepted by the angle and its vertical angle.

$$m\angle 1 = \frac{1}{2}(m\widehat{PR} + m\widehat{QS})$$

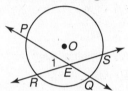

- If a secant and a tangent intersect at the point of tangency, then the measure of each angle formed is one-half the measure of its intercepted arc.

$$m\angle XTV = \frac{1}{2}m\widehat{TUV}$$
$$m\angle YTV = \frac{1}{2}m\widehat{TV}$$

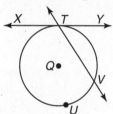

Example 1 Find x.

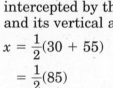

The two secants intersect inside the circle, so x is equal to one-half the sum of the measures of the arcs intercepted by the angle and its vertical angle.

$$x = \frac{1}{2}(30 + 55)$$
$$= \frac{1}{2}(85)$$
$$= 42.5$$

Example 2 Find y.

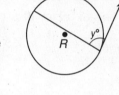

The secant and the tangent intersect at the point of tangency, so the measure of the angle is one-half the measure of its intercepted arc.

$$y = \frac{1}{2}(168)$$
$$= 84$$

Exercises

Find each measure.

1. $m\angle 1$

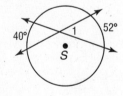

2. $m\angle 2$

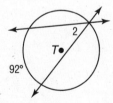

3. $m\angle 3$

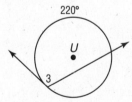

4. $m\angle 4$

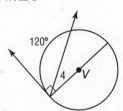

5. $m\angle 5$

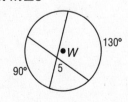

6. $m\angle 6$

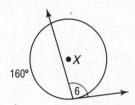

10-6 Study Guide and Intervention (continued)

Secants, Tangents, and Angle Measures

Intersections Outside a Circle If secants and tangents intersect outside a circle, they form an angle whose measure is related to the intercepted arcs.

If two secants, a secant and a tangent, or two tangents intersect in the exterior of a circle, then the measure of the angle formed is one-half the positive difference of the measures of the intercepted arcs.

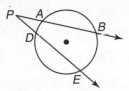

$\overrightarrow{PB}$ and $\overrightarrow{PE}$ are secants.
$m\angle P = \frac{1}{2}(m\widehat{BE} - m\widehat{AD})$

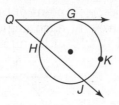

$\overrightarrow{QG}$ is a tangent. $\overrightarrow{QJ}$ is a secant.
$m\angle Q = \frac{1}{2}(m\widehat{GKJ} - m\widehat{GH})$

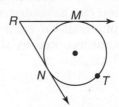

$\overrightarrow{RM}$ and $\overrightarrow{RN}$ are tangents.
$m\angle R = \frac{1}{2}(m\widehat{MTN} - m\widehat{MN})$

Example Find $m\angle MPN$.

$\angle MPN$ is formed by two secants that intersect in the exterior of a circle.

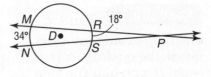

$m\angle MPN = \frac{1}{2}(m\widehat{MN} - m\widehat{RS})$

$= \frac{1}{2}(34 - 18)$

$= \frac{1}{2}(16)$ or 8

The measure of the angle is 8.

Exercises

Find each measure.

1. $m\angle 1$

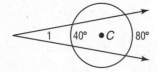

2. $m\angle 2$

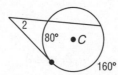

3. $m\angle 3$

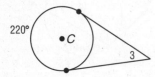

4. x

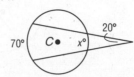

5. x

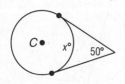

6. x

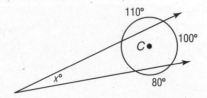

10-6 Skills Practice

Secants, Tangents, and Angle Measures

Find each measure.

1. $m\angle 1$

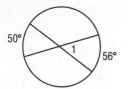

2. $m\angle 2$

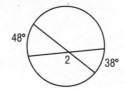

3. $m\angle 3$

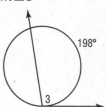

4. $m\angle 4$

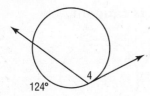

5. $m\angle 5$

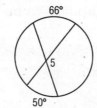

6. $m\angle 6$

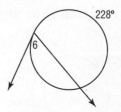

Find x. Assume that any segment that appears to be tangent is tangent.

7.

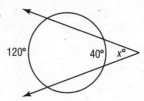

8.

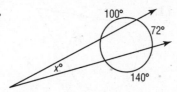

9.

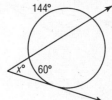

10.

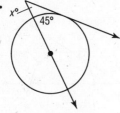

11.

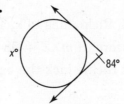

12.

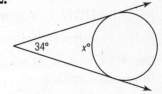

Lesson 10-6

10-6 Practice

Secants, Tangents, and Angle Measures

Find each measure.

1. $m\angle 1$

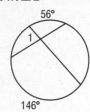

56°
1
146°

2. $m\angle 2$

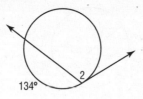

2
134°

3. $m\angle 3$

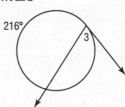

216°
3

Find x. Assume that any segment that appears to be tangent is tangent.

7.

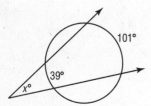

101°
39°
$x°$

8.

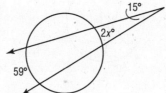

15°
$2x°$
59°

9.

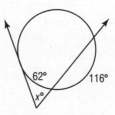

62°
116°
$x°$

10.

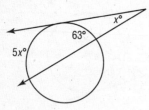

$x°$
63°
$5x°$

11.

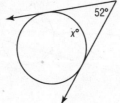

52°
$x°$

12.

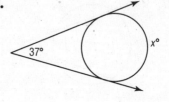

37°
$x°$

9. RECREATION In a game of kickball, Rickie has to kick the
ball through a semicircular goal to score. If $m\widehat{XZ} = 58$ and
the $m\widehat{XY} = 122$, at what angle must Rickie kick the ball
to score? Explain.

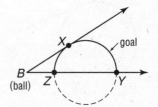

X
goal
B
(ball)
Z
Y

10-6 **Word Problem Practice**

Secants, Tangents, and Angle Measures

1. **TELESCOPES** Vanessa looked through her telescope at a mountainous landscape. The figure shows what she saw. Based on the view, approximately what angle does the side of the mountain that runs from A to B make with the horizontal?

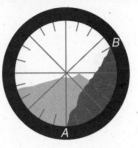

2. **RADAR** Two airplanes were tracked on radar. They followed the paths shown in the figure.

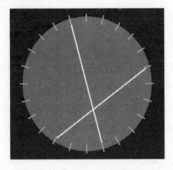

What is the acute angle between their flight paths?

3. **EASELS** Francisco is a painter. He places a circular canvas on his A-frame easel and carefully centers it. The apex of the easel is 30° and the measure of arc BC is 22°. What is the measure of arc AB?

4. **FLYING** When flying at an altitude of 5 miles, the lines of sight to the horizon looking north and south make about a 173.7° angle. How much of the longitude line directly under the plane is visible from 5 miles high?

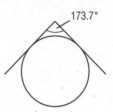

STAINED GLASS For Exercises 5 and 6, use the following information.

Pablo made the stained glass window shown. He used an inscribed square and equilateral triangle for the design.

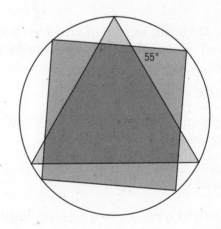

5. Label the angle measures on the outer edge of the triangle.

6. Label all of the arcs with their degree measure.

10-6 Enrichment

Orbiting Bodies

The path of the Earth's orbit around the sun is elliptical. However, it is often viewed as circular.

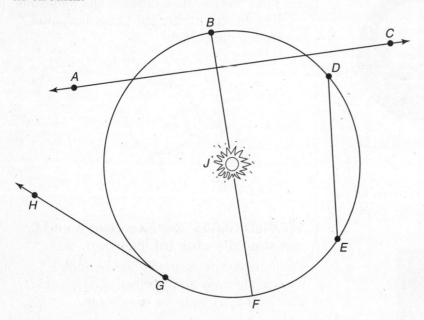

Use the drawing above of the Earth orbiting the sun to name the line or segment described. Then identify it as a *radius*, *diameter*, *chord*, *tangent*, or *secant* of the orbit.

1. the path of an asteroid

2. the distance between the Earth's position in July and the Earth's position in October

3. the distance between the Earth's position in December and the Earth's position in June

4. the path of a rocket shot toward Saturn

5. the path of a sunbeam

6. If a planet has a moon, the moon circles the planet as the planet circles the sun. To visualize the path of the moon, cut two circles from a piece of cardboard, one with a diameter of 4 inches and one with a diameter of 1 inch.

Tape the larger circle firmly to a piece of paper. Poke a pencil point through the smaller circle, close to the edge. Roll the small circle around the outside of the large one. The pencil will trace out the path of a moon circling its planet. This kind of curve is called an epicycloid. To see the path of the planet around the sun, poke the pencil through the center of the small circle (the planet), and roll the small circle around the large one (the sun).

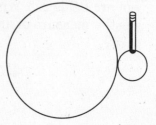

10-7 Lesson Reading Guide

Special Segments in a Circle

Get Ready for the Lesson

Read the introduction to Lesson 10-7 in your textbook.

- What kinds of angles of the circle are formed at the points of the star?

- What is the sum of the measures of the five angles of the star?

Read the Lesson

1. Refer to ⊙O. Name each of the following.

   a. a diameter

   b. a chord that is not a diameter

   c. two chords that intersect in the interior of the circle

   d. an exterior point

   e. two secant segments that intersect in the exterior of the circle

   f. a tangent segment

   g. a right angle

   h. an external secant segment

   i. a secant-tangent angle with vertex on the circle

   j. an inscribed angle

2. Supply the missing length to complete each equation.

   a. $BH \cdot HD = FH \cdot$ _____   **b.** $AC \cdot AF = AD \cdot$ _____

   c. $AD \cdot AE = AB \cdot$ _____   **d.** $AB =$ _____

   e. $AF \cdot AC = ($_____$)^2$ **f.** $EG \cdot$ _____ $= FG \cdot GC$

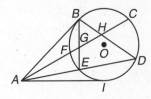

Remember What You Learned

3. Some students find it easier to remember geometric theorems if they restate them in their own words. Restate Theorem 10.16 in a way that you find easier to remember.

10-7 Study Guide and Intervention

Special Segments in a Circle

Segments Intersecting Inside a Circle If two chords intersect in a circle, then the products of the measures of the chords are equal.

$$a \cdot b = c \cdot d$$

Example Find x.

The two chords intersect inside the circle, so the products $AB \cdot BC$ and $EB \cdot BD$ are equal.

$$AB \cdot BC = EB \cdot BD$$

$6 \cdot x = 8 \cdot 3$	Substitution
$6x = 24$	Simplify.
$x = 4$	Divide each side by 6.

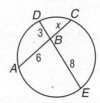

$AB \cdot BC = EB \cdot BD$

Exercises

Find x to the nearest tenth.

1.

2.

3.

4.

5.

6.

7.

8.

10-7 Study Guide and Intervention *(continued)*

Special Segments in a Circle

Segments Intersecting Outside a Circle If secants and tangents intersect outside a circle, then two products are equal.

- If two secant segments are drawn to a circle from an exterior point, then the product of the measures of one secant segment and its external secant segment is equal to the product of the measures of the other secant segment and its external secant segment.

- If a tangent segment and a secant segment are drawn to a circle from an exterior point, then the square of the measure of the tangent segment is equal to the product of the measures of the secant segment and its external secant segment.

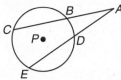

$\overline{AC}$ and $\overline{AE}$ are secant segments.
$\overline{AB}$ and $\overline{AD}$ are external secant segments.
$AC \cdot AB = AE \cdot AD$

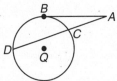

$\overline{AB}$ is a tangent segment.
$\overline{AD}$ is a secant segment.
$\overline{AC}$ is an external secant segment.
$(AB)^2 = AD \cdot AC$

Example Find x to the nearest tenth.

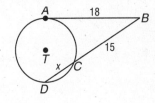

The tangent segment is $\overline{AB}$, the secant segment is $\overline{BD}$, and the external secant segment is $\overline{BC}$.

$(AB)^2 = BC \cdot BD$
$(18)^2 = 15(15 + x)$
$324 = 225 + 15x$
$99 = 15x$
$6.6 = x$

Exercises

Find x to the nearest tenth. Assume segments that appear to be tangent are tangent.

1.
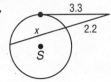

2.
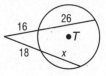

3.

4.
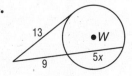

5.
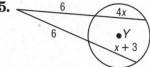

6.
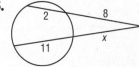

7.

8.

9.
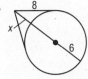

Lesson 10-7

10-7 Skills Practice

Special Segments in a Circle

Find x to the nearest tenth if necessary. Assume that segments that appear to be tangent are tangent.

1.
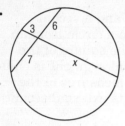

2.
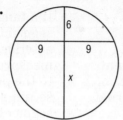

3.
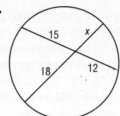

4.
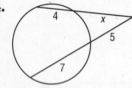

5.
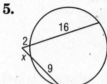

6.
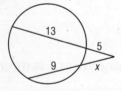

7.
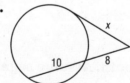

8.
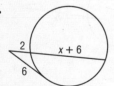

9.
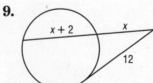

NAME _____ DATE _____ PERIOD _____

Special Segments in a Circle

Find *x* to the nearest tenth if necessary. Assume that segments that appear to be
tangent are tangent.

1.   2.   3.

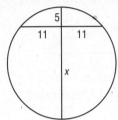   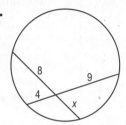   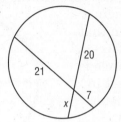

4.   5.

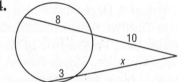   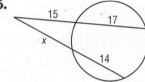

6.   7.

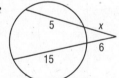   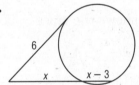

8.   9.

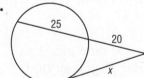   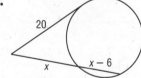

10. **CONSTRUCTION** An arch over an apartment entrance is
3 feet high and 9 feet wide. Find the radius of the circle
containing the arc of the arch.

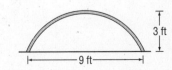

Chapter 10   53   *Glencoe Geometry*

10-7 Word Problem Practice

Special Segments in a Circle

1. **ICE SKATING** Ted skated through one of the face-off circles at a skating rink. His path through the circle is shown in the figure. Given that the face-off circle is 15 feet in diameter, what distance within the face-off circle did Ted travel?

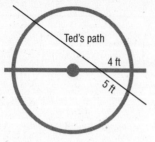

Ted's path
4 ft
5 ft

2. **HORIZONS** Assume that Earth is a perfect sphere with a diameter of 7926 miles. From an altitude of a miles, how long is the horizon line h?

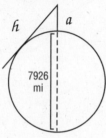

h a
7926 mi

3. **AXLES** The figure shows the cross-section of an axle held in place by a triangular sleeve. A brake extends from the apex of the triangle. When the brake is extended 2.5 inches into the sleeve, it comes into contact with the axle. What is the diameter of the axle?

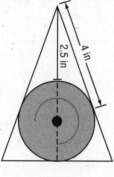

2.5 in
4 in

4. **ARCHEOLOGY** Scientists unearthed part of a circular wall. They made the measurements shown in the figure.

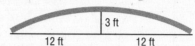

3 ft
12 ft   12 ft

Based on the information in the figure, what was the radius of the circle?

PIZZA DELIVERY For Exercises 5 and 6, use the following information.

Pizza Power is located at the intersection of Northern Boulevard and Highway 1 in a city with a circular highway running all the way around its outskirts. The radius of the circular highway is 13 miles. Pizza Power puts the map shown below on its take-out menus.

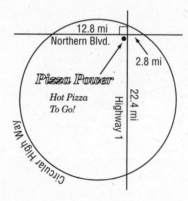

12.8 mi
Northern Blvd.
2.8 mi
Pizza Power
Hot Pizza
To Go!
Highway 1
22.4 mi
Circular High Way

5. How many miles away is the Circular Highway from Pizza Power if you travel north on Highway 1?

6. The city builds a new road along the diameter of Circular Highway that passes through the intersection of Northern Boulevard and Highway 1. Along this new road, about how many miles is it (the shorter way) to the Circular Highway from Pizza Power?

10-7 Enrichment

The Nine-Point Circle

The figure below illustrates a surprising fact about triangles and circles. Given any $\triangle ABC$, there is a circle that contains all of the following nine points:

(1) the midpoints K, L, and M of the sides of $\triangle ABC$

(2) the points X, Y, and Z, where $\overline{AX}$, $\overline{BY}$, and $\overline{CZ}$ are the altitudes of $\triangle ABC$

(3) the points R, S, and T which are the midpoints of the segments $\overline{AH}$, $\overline{BH}$, and $\overline{CH}$ that join the vertices of $\triangle ABC$ to the point H where the lines containing the altitudes intersect.

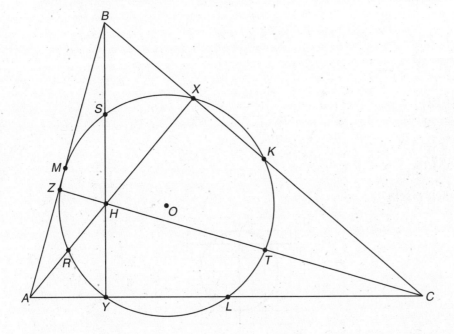

1. On a separate sheet of paper, draw an obtuse triangle ABC. Use your straightedge and compass to construct the circle passing through the midpoints of the sides. Be careful to make your construction as accurate as possible. Does your circle contain the other six points described above?

2. In the figure you constructed for Exercise 1, draw $\overline{RK}$, $\overline{SL}$, and $\overline{TM}$. What do you observe?

10-8 Lesson Reading Guide

Equations of Circles

Get Ready for the Lesson

Read the introduction to Lesson 10-8 in your textbook.

In a series of concentric circles, what is the same about all the circles, and what is different?

Read the Lesson

1. Identify the center and radius of each circle.

　a. $(x - 2)^2 + (y - 3)^2 = 16$　　　　**b.** $(x + 1)^2 + (y + 5)^2 = 9$

　c. $x^2 + y^2 = 49$　　　　　　　　　　**d.** $(x - 8)^2 + (y + 1)^2 = 36$

　e. $x^2 + (y - 10)^2 = 144$　　　　　　**f.** $(x + 3)^2 + y^2 = 5$

2. Write an equation for each circle.

　a. center at origin, $r = 8$

　b. center at $(3, 9)$, $r = 1$

　c. center at $(-5, -6)$, $r = 10$

　d. center at $(0, -7)$, $r = 7$

　e. center at $(12, 0)$, $d = 12$

　f. center at $(-4, 8)$, $d = 22$

　g. center at $(4.5, -3.5)$, $r = 1.5$

　h. center at $(0, 0)$, $r = \sqrt{13}$

3. Write an equation for each circle.

a.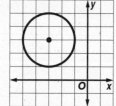

b.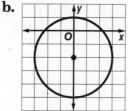

c.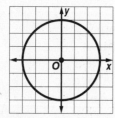

d.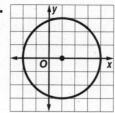

Remember What You Learned

4. A good way to remember a new mathematical formula or equation is to relate it to one you already know. How can you use the Distance Formula to help you remember the standard equation of a circle?

10-8 Study Guide and Intervention

Equations of Circles

Equation of a Circle A **circle** is the locus of points in a
plane equidistant from a given point. You can use this definition
to write an equation of a circle.

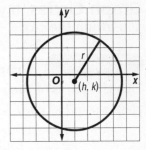

Standard Equation of a Circle	An equation for a circle with center at (h, k) and a radius of r units is $(x - h)^2 + (y - k)^2 = r^2$.

Example **Write an equation for a circle with center $(-1, 3)$ and radius 6.**
Use the formula $(x - h)^2 + (y - k)^2 = r^2$ with $h = -1$, $k = 3$, and $r = 6$.

$$(x - h)^2 + (y - k)^2 = r^2 \quad \text{Equation of a circle}$$
$$(x - (-1))^2 + (y - 3)^2 = 6^2 \quad \text{Substitution}$$
$$(x + 1)^2 + (y - 3)^2 = 36 \quad \text{Simplify.}$$

Exercises

Write an equation for each circle.

1. center at $(0, 0)$, $r = 8$

2. center at $(-2, 3)$, $r = 5$

3. center at $(2, -4)$, $r = 1$

4. center at $(-1, -4)$, $r = 2$

5. center at $(-2, -6)$, diameter $= 8$

6. center at $\left(-\dfrac{1}{2}, \dfrac{1}{4}\right)$, $r = \sqrt{3}$

7. center at the origin, diameter $= 4$

8. center at $\left(1, -\dfrac{5}{8}\right)$, $r = \sqrt{5}$

9. Find the center and radius of a circle with equation $x^2 + y^2 = 20$.

10. Find the center and radius of a circle with equation $(x + 4)^2 + (y + 3)^2 = 16$.

Lesson 10-8

10-8 Study Guide and Intervention *(continued)*

Equations of Circles

Graph Circles If you are given an equation of a circle, you can find information to help you graph the circle.

Example **Graph $(x + 3)^2 + (y - 1)^2 = 9$.**

Use the parts of the equation to find (h, k) and r.

$(x - h)^2 + (y - k)^2 = r^2$

$\quad (x - h)^2 = (x + 3)^2 \qquad (y - k)^2 = (y - 1)^2 \qquad r^2 = 9$

$\qquad x - h = x + 3 \qquad\qquad y - k = y - 1 \qquad\qquad r = 3$

$\qquad\quad -h = 3 \qquad\qquad\qquad -k = -1$

$\qquad\qquad h = -3 \qquad\qquad\qquad k = 1$

The center is at $(-3, 1)$ and the radius is 3. Graph the center.
Use a compass set at a radius of 3 grid squares to draw the circle.

Exercises

Graph each equation.

1. $x^2 + y^2 = 16$

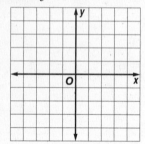

2. $(x - 2)^2 + (y - 1)^2 = 9$

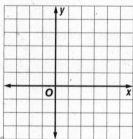

3. $(x + 2)^2 + y^2 = 16$

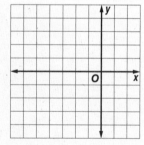

4. $(x + 1)^2 + (y - 2)^2 = 6.25$

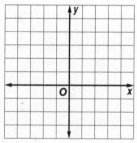

5. $\left(x + \frac{1}{2}\right)^2 + \left(y - \frac{1}{4}\right)^2 = 4$

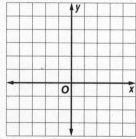

6. $x^2 + (y - 1)^2 = 9$

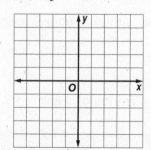

10-8 Skills Practice

Equations of Circles

Write an equation for each circle.

1. center at origin, $r = 6$

2. center at $(0, 0)$, $r = 2$

3. center at $(4, 3)$, $r = 9$

4. center at $(7, 1)$, $d = 24$

5. center at $(-5, 2)$, $r = 4$

6. center at $(6, -8)$, $d = 10$

7. a circle with center at $(8, 4)$ and a radius with endpoint $(0, 4)$

8. a circle with center at $(-2, -7)$ and a radius with endpoint $(0, 7)$

9. a circle with center at $(-3, 9)$ and a radius with endpoint $(1, 9)$

10. a circle whose diameter has endpoints $(-3, 0)$ and $(3, 0)$

Graph each equation.

11. $x^2 + y^2 = 16$

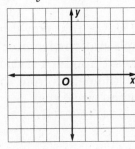

12. $(x - 1)^2 + (y - 4)^2 = 9$

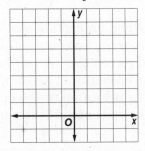

Glencoe Geometry

10-8 Practice

Equations of Circles

Write an equation for each circle.

1. center at origin, $r = 7$

2. center at $(0, 0)$, $d = 18$

3. center at $(-7, 11)$, $r = 8$

4. center at $(12, -9)$, $d = 22$

5. center at $(-6, -4)$, $r = \sqrt{5}$

6. center at $(3, 0)$, $d = 28$

7. a circle with center at $(-5, 3)$ and a radius with endpoint $(2, 3)$

8. a circle whose diameter has endpoints $(4, 6)$ and $(-2, 6)$

Graph each equation.

9. $x^2 + y^2 = 4$

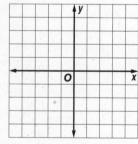

10. $(x + 3)^2 + (y - 3)^2 = 9$

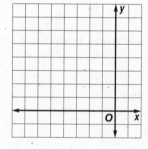

11. EARTHQUAKES When an earthquake strikes, it releases seismic waves that travel in concentric circles from the epicenter of the earthquake. Seismograph stations monitor seismic activity and record the intensity and duration of earthquakes. Suppose a station determines that the epicenter of an earthquake is located about 50 kilometers from the station. If the station is located at the origin, write an equation for the circle that represents a possible epicenter of the earthquake.

10-8 Word Problem Practice

Equations of Circles

1. **DESIGN** Arthur wants to write the equation of a circle that is inscribed in the square shown in the graph.

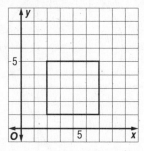

   What is the equation of the desired circle?

2. **DRAFTING** The design for a park is drawn on a coordinate graph. The perimeter of the park is modeled by the equation $(x - 3)^2 + (x - 7)^2 = 225$. Each unit on the graph represents 10 feet. What is the radius of the actual park?

3. **WALLPAPER** The design of a piece of wallpaper consists of circles that can be modeled by the equation $(x - a)^2 + (y - b)^2 = 4$, for all even integers b. Sketch part of the wallpaper on a grid.

4. **SECURITY RING** A circular safety ring surrounds a top-secret laboratory. On one map of the laboratory grounds, the safety ring is given by the equation $x^2 + y^2 - 20x + 14y = 175$. Each unit on the map represents 1 mile. What is the radius of the safety ring?

DISTANCE For Exercises 5-7, use the following information.

Cleo lives the same distance from the library, the post office, and her school. The table below gives the coordinates of these places on a map with a coordinate grid where one unit represents one yard.

Location	Coordinates
Library	$(-78, 202)$
Post Office	$(111, 193)$
School	$(202, -106)$

5. What are the coordinates of Cleo's home? Sketch the circle on a map locating all three places and Cleo's home.

6. How far is Cleo's house from the places mentioned?

7. Write an equation for the circle that passes through the library, post office, and school.

Lesson 10-8

10-8 Enrichment

Equations of Circles and Tangents

Recall that the circle whose radius is r and whose center has coordinates (h, k) is the graph of $(x - h)^2 + (y - k)^2 = r^2$. You can use this idea and what you know about circles and tangents to find an equation of the circle that has a given center and is tangent to a given line.

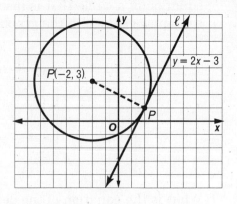

Use the following steps to find an equation for the circle that has center $C(-2, 3)$ and is tangent to the graph $y = 2x - 3$. Refer to the figure.

1. State the slope of the line ℓ that has equation $y = 2x - 3$.

2. Suppose $\odot C$ with center $C(-2, 3)$ is tangent to line ℓ at point P. What is the slope of radius $\overline{CP}$?

3. Find an equation for the line that contains $\overline{CP}$.

4. Use your equation from Exercise 3 and the equation $y = 2x - 3$. At what point do the lines for these equations intersect? What are its coordinates?

5. Find the measure of radius $\overline{CP}$.

6. Use the coordinate pair $C(-2, 3)$ and your answer for Exercise 5 to write an equation for $\odot C$.

10 Student Recording Sheet

Read each question. Then fill in the correct answer.

1. Ⓐ Ⓑ Ⓒ Ⓓ

2. Ⓕ Ⓖ Ⓗ Ⓙ

3. Record your answer and fill in the bubbles in the grid below. Be sure to use the correct place value.

4. Ⓐ Ⓑ Ⓒ Ⓓ

5. Ⓕ Ⓖ Ⓗ Ⓙ

6. Ⓐ Ⓑ Ⓒ Ⓓ

7. Ⓕ Ⓖ Ⓗ Ⓙ

8. Ⓐ Ⓑ Ⓒ Ⓓ

9. Ⓕ Ⓖ Ⓗ Ⓙ

10. Ⓐ Ⓑ Ⓒ Ⓓ

Pre-AP

Record your answers for Question 11 on the back of this paper.

Assessment

10 Rubric for Scoring Pre-AP

General Scoring Guidelines

- If a student gives only a correct numerical answer to a problem but does not show how he or she arrived at the answer, the student will be awarded only 1 credit. All extended response questions require the student to show work.

- A fully correct answer for a multiple-part question requires correct responses for all parts of the question. For example, if a question has three parts, the correct response to one or two parts of the question that required work to be shown is *not* considered a fully correct response.

- Students who use trial and error to solve a problem must show their method. Merely showing that the answer checks or is correct is not considered a complete response for full credit.

Exercise 13 Rubric

Score	Specific Criteria
4	A correct solution that is supported by well-developed, accurate explanations. The graph is complete with labels. The center of the circle is $(1, 2)$. The radius is 4. The circumference of the circle is 8π units. The equation of the circle is $(x - 1)^2 + (y - 2)^2$.
3	A generally correct solution, but may contain minor flaws in reasoning or computation.
2	A partially correct interpretation and/or solution to the problem.
1	A correct solution with no supporting evidence or explanation.
0	An incorrect solution indicating no mathematical understanding of the concept or task, or no solution is given.

10 Chapter 10 Quiz 1

(Lessons 10–1 and 10–2)

SCORE _____

1. In $\odot A$, find CE if $BA = 4$.

1. _____8_____

2. Find the circumference of $\odot X$ to the nearest hundredth.

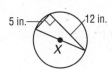

2. ____40.84 in.____

3. Circle **T** has diameters $\overline{QS}$ and $\overline{PR}$. Find $m\widehat{RS}$.

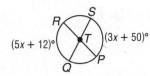

3. _____73°_____

4. The diameter of a clock's face is 6 inches. Find the length of the minor arc formed by the hands of the clock at 4:00. Round to the nearest hundredth.

4. ____6.28 in.____

5. **MULTIPLE CHOICE** Find the circumference of $\odot O$ to the nearest hundredth.

A. 4.00 in.   C. 12.57 in.
B. 8.00 in.   D. 25.13 in.

5. _____D_____

- -

10 Chapter 10 Quiz 2

(Lessons 10–3 and 10–4)

SCORE _____

1. In $\odot O$, $PQ = 20$, $RS = 20$, and $m\widehat{PT} = 35$. Find $m\widehat{RS}$.

1. _____70°_____

2. Determine the radius of a circle if a 24-inch chord is 9 inches from the center.

2. ____15 in.____

3. Find x.

3. _____22_____

4. A regular hexagon is inscribed in a circle with a radius of 12 centimeters. Find the measure of each side of the hexagon.

4. ____12 cm____

5. Each side of an inscribed equilateral triangle measures 18 cm. Find the length of one of the minor arcs. Round to the nearest hundredth.

5. ____21.77 cm____

Assessment

10 Chapter 10 Quiz 3

(Lessons 10–5 and 10–6)

1. Two segments from P are tangent to $\odot O$. If $m\angle P = 60$ and the radius of $\odot O$ is 12 feet, find the length of each tangent.

1. _____ **$12\sqrt{3}$ ft** _____

2. Determine whether the converse of the statement is *true* or *false*.

If two segments from the same exterior point are tangent to a circle, then they are congruent.

2. _____ **false** _____

For Questions 3–5, use $\odot E$ with $\overleftrightarrow{CG}$ tangent at C.

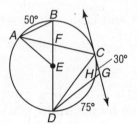

3. Find $m\angle ABD$.

3. _____ **65°** _____

4. Find $m\angle AFB$.

4. _____ **77.5°** _____

5. Find $m\angle CGD$.

5. _____ **112.5°** _____

- -

10 Chapter 10 Quiz 4

(Lessons 10–7 and 10–8)

1. Find x.

1. _____ **4** _____

2. If $\overrightarrow{AB}$ is tangent to $\odot P$ at B, find x and y.

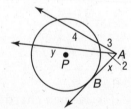

2. _____ $x = \sqrt{21},\ y = \dfrac{17}{2}$ _____

3. Find the coordinates of the center of a circle whose equation is $(x + 11)^2 + (y - 13)^2 = 4$.

3. _____ **(−11, 13)** _____

4. Determine the radius of a circle with an equation of $(x + 12)^2 + (y + 3)^2 = 225$.

4. _____ **15** _____

5. Graph $x^2 + (y - 1)^2 = 9$.

5.

10 Chapter 10 Mid-Chapter Test

SCORE _____

(Lessons 10–1 through 10–4)

Part I *Write the letter for the correct answer in the blank at the right of each question.*

1. What is the name of the longest chord in a circle?
   A. diameter   **B.** radius   **C.** secant   **D.** tangent

1. _____

2. The radius of ⊙*B* is 4 centimeters and the circumference of ⊙*A* is 20π centimeters. Find *CD*.
   F. 10 cm   **H.** 24 cm
   G. 14 cm   **J.** 28 cm

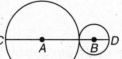

2. _____

3. A chord of ⊙*P* measures 8 inches and the distance from the center to the chord is 3 inches. Find the radius of ⊙*P*.
   A. 3 in.   **B.** 5 in.   **C.** $\sqrt{73}$ in.   **D.** 10 in.

3. _____

4. If $m\angle MON = 86°$, find $m\angle MPN$.
   F. 86°   **H.** 43°
   G. 45°   **J.** 30°

4. _____

5. Find *x* if $m\angle 1 = 2x + 10$ and $m\angle 2 = 3x - 6$.
   A. 4   **C.** 24
   B. 16   **D.** 42

5. _____

Part II

6. $\overline{AE}$ is a diameter of ⊙*G* and $m\angle BGE = 136°$. Find $m\widehat{AB}$.

6. _____

7. A circle with a radius of 12 inches has an arc that measures 8π inches. Find the measure of the central angle determined by this arc.

7. _____

8. In ⊙*P*, chord $\overline{AB}$ measures $4x - 6$ centimeters and chord $\overline{CD}$ measures $6x - 12$ centimeters. If $\overline{AB}$ and $\overline{CD}$ are each 4 centimeters from *P*, find *AP*.

8. _____

9. A 15-inch by 8-inch tablecloth is placed on a circular table. Each of the four corners of the tablecloth touch the edge of the table. Determine the radius of the table.

9. _____

10. Quadrilateral *ABCD* is inscribed in ⊙*P*. Find $m\angle ABC$.

10. _____

10 Chapter 10 Vocabulary Test

arc	circumscribed	pi (π)
center	diameter	point of tangency
central angle	inscribed	radius
chord	intercepted	secant
circle	major arc	semicircle
circumference	minor arc	tangent

State whether each sentence is *true* or *false*. If false, replace the underlined word or number to make a true sentence.

1. The vertex of a(n) <u>central</u> angle lies on the circle.

1. _____

2. A(n) <u>circle</u> is the locus of all points in a plane equidistant from a given point.

2. _____

3. $C = 2\pi r$ is the formula for the <u>circumference</u> of a circle.

3. _____

4. The <u>diameter</u> of a circle is a segment with one endpoint at the center and the other endpoint on the circle.

4. _____

5. A <u>major arc</u> has measure greater than 0 but less than 180.

5. _____

Choose the correct term to complete each sentence.

6. The point of tangency is the point where a (*secant* or *tangent*) intersects a circle.

6. _____

7. A (*secant* or *chord*) is a line that intersects a circle in two points.

7. _____

Choose from the terms above to complete each sentence.

8. A(n) _____ is a line that intersects a circle in one point.

8. _____

9. A(n) _____ is an arc that measures 180°.

9. _____

10. _____ is an irrational number equal to the ratio of the circumference to the diameter of a circle.

10. _____

Define each term in your own words.

11. congruent arcs

11. _____

12. circumscribed polygon

12. _____

10   Chapter 10 Test, Form 1

Write the letter for the correct answer in the blank at the right of each question.

For Questions 1–3, use ⊙X.

1. Name a radius.
   A. $\overline{XB}$ **B.** $\overline{AB}$ **C.** $\overline{BC}$ **D.** $\overleftrightarrow{AC}$

1. _____

2. Name a chord.
   F. $\overline{XB}$ **G.** $\overline{XC}$ **H.** $\overline{BC}$ **J.** $\overrightarrow{AC}$

2. _____

3. Name a tangent.
   A. $\overline{AB}$ **B.** $\overline{BC}$ **C.** $\overrightarrow{AC}$ **D.** $\overrightarrow{BD}$

3. _____

4. The wheels on Elliot's truck each have a circumference of 22 inches. Determine the radius of each wheel.
   F. 2.5 in.   **G.** 3.5 in.   **H.** 5 in.   **J.** 7 in.

4. _____

5. In ⊙C, $m\widehat{AB} = 72$. Find $m\angle BCD$.
   A. 72   **C.** 144
   B. 108   **D.** 180

5. _____

6. Find the length of $\widehat{PQ}$ in ⊙R to the nearest hundredth.
   F. 9.42 m   **H.** 3.14 m
   G. 4.71 m   **J.** 1.57 m

6. _____

7. In ⊙O, $AB = 12$ centimeters, $OE = 4$ centimeters, and $OF = 4$ centimeters. Find CF.
   A. 6 cm   **C.** 12 cm
   B. 8 cm   **D.** 24 cm

7. _____

8. Find the radius of a circle if a 48-meter chord is 7 meters from the center.
   F. 14 m   **G.** 24 m   **H.** 25 m   **J.** 41 m

8. _____

9. Find $m\angle ABC$.
   A. 50   **C.** 90
   B. 70   **D.** 140

9. _____

10. If $m\angle X = 126$, find $m\angle Z$.
    F. 54   **H.** 90
    G. 63   **J.** 126

10. _____

11. If $\overline{MN}$, $\overline{NO}$, and $\overline{MO}$ are tangent to ⊙P, find x.
    A. 2 m   **C.** 6 m
    B. 5 m   **D.** 8 m

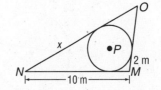

11. _____

Assessment

10 **Chapter 10 Test, Form 1** *(continued)*

12. Find x.
F. 122
G. 95
H. 68
J. 61

12. _____

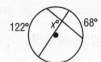

13. Find y.
A. 16
B. 56
C. 80
D. 112

13. _____

14. Find z.
F. 38
G. 56
H. 58
J. 76

14. _____

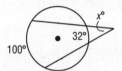

15. Find x.
A. 132
B. 68
C. 66
D. 34

15. _____

16. Find y.
F. 18
G. 12
H. 6
J. 4.5

16. _____

17. Find z.
A. 11.25
B. 10
C. 7.5
D. 4

17. _____

18. Find the radius of the circle whose equation is $(x + 3)^2 + (y - 7)^2 = 289$.
F. 7   G. 17   H. 34   J. 289

18. _____

19. Find the equation of a circle with center $(0 , 0)$ and radius 4.
A. $x^2 + y^2 = 4$
B. $x^2 + y^2 = 16$
C. $(x - 4)^2 + (y - 4)^2 = 16$
D. $4x + 4y = 16$

19. _____

20. Identify the graph of $(x - 3)^2 + (y + 2)^2 = 4$.
F.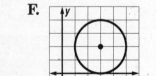
G.
H.
J.

20. _____

Bonus Find x.

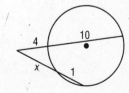

B: _____

10 **Chapter 10 Test, Form 2A** SCORE _____

Write the letter for the correct answer in the blank at the right of each question.

For Questions 1–3, use ⊙O.

1. Name a diameter.
   A. $\overline{FG}$
   B. $\overline{AB}$
   C. $\overrightarrow{AB}$
   D. $\overleftrightarrow{CE}$

   1. _____

2. Name a chord.
   F. $\overline{FO}$
   G. $\overline{AB}$
   H. $\overrightarrow{AB}$
   J. $\overleftrightarrow{CE}$

   2. _____

3. Name a secant.
   A. $\overline{FO}$
   B. $\overline{AB}$
   C. $\overrightarrow{AB}$
   D. $\overleftrightarrow{CE}$

   3. _____

4. The diameter of a circular swimming pool is 15 feet. Find the circumference to the nearest hundredth.
   F. 47.12 ft
   G. 63.81 ft
   H. 75.96 ft
   J. 94.24 ft

   4. _____

5. In ⊙A, $m\angle BAD = 110$. Find $m\widehat{DE}$.
   A. 35
   B. 55
   C. 70
   D. 110

   5. _____

6. Points X and Y lie on ⊙P so that $PX = 5$ meters and $m\angle XPY = 90$. Find the length of $\widehat{XY}$ to the nearest hundredth.
   F. 3.93 m
   G. 7.85 m
   H. 15.71 m
   J. 19.63 m

   6. _____

7. Chords $\overline{XY}$ and $\overline{WV}$ are equidistant from the center of ⊙O. If $XY = 2x + 30$ and $WV = 5x - 12$, find x.
   A. 58
   B. 28
   C. 14
   D. 6

   7. _____

8. Find the radius of ⊙O if $DE = 12$ inches and $\overline{DE}$ bisects $\overline{OF}$.
   F. $2\sqrt{3}$ in.
   G. 6 in.
   H. 8 in.
   J. $4\sqrt{3}$ in.

   8. _____

9. Find x.
   A. 122
   B. 61
   C. 58
   D. 29

   9. _____

10. *EFGH* is a quadrilateral inscribed in ⊙P with $m\angle E = 72$ and $m\angle F = 49$. Find $m\angle H$.
    F. 131
    G. 108
    H. 90
    J. 57

    10. _____

11. If $\overline{AB}$ is tangent to ⊙C at A, find BC.
    A. 6 in.
    B. $4\sqrt{3}$ in.
    C. $12\sqrt{3}$ in.
    D. 24 in.

    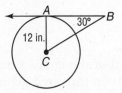

    11. _____

Assessment

12. $\overline{PQ}$, $\overline{QR}$, $\overline{RS}$, and $\overline{SP}$ are tangent to $\odot X$. Find RS.   12. _____

    F. 9 in.   **H.** 13 in.

    G. 12 in.   **J.** cannot tell

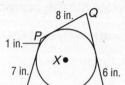

13. Circle A has its center at $A(3, 2)$, and $\overleftrightarrow{CB}$ is tangent to $\odot A$ at $B(6, 4)$. Find the   13. _____
slope of $\overleftrightarrow{CB}$.

    A. 1   **B.** $\frac{1}{2}$ **C.** $-\frac{3}{2}$ **D.** $-\frac{1}{2}$

14. Find x.   14. _____

    F. 78   **H.** 102

    G. 90   **J.** 156

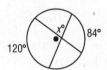

15. Find y.   15. _____

    A. 66   **C.** 45

    B. 57   **D.** 21

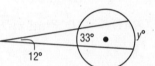

16. Find z.   16. _____

    F. 2   **H.** 7

    G. 4.5   **J.** 8

17. Find x.   17. _____

    A. 4   **C.** 22

    B. 16   **D.** 32

18. Find the center of the circle whose equation is $(x + 11)^2 + (y - 7)^2 = 121$.   18. _____

    F. $(-11, 7)$ **G.** $(11, -7)$ **H.** $(121, 49)$ **J.** 11

19. Find the equation of a circle whose center is at $(2, 3)$ and radius is 6.   19. _____

    A. $(x + 2)^2 + (y + 3)^2 = 6$ **C.** $(x + 2)^2 + (y + 3)^2 = 36$

    B. $(x - 2)^2 + (y - 3)^2 = 6$ **D.** $(x - 2)^2 + (y - 3)^2 = 36$

20. Find the equation of $\odot P$.   20. _____

    F. $x^2 + (y - 3)^2 = 4$ **H.** $(x - 3)^2 + y^2 = 2$

    G. $x^2 + (y - 3)^2 = 2$ **J.** $(x - 3)^2 + y^2 = 4$

Bonus A chord of the circle whose equation is $x^2 + y^2 = 57$ is   **B:** _____
tangent to the circle whose equation is $x^2 + y^2 = 32$ at
the point $(4, -4)$. Find the length of the chord.

10 Chapter 10 Test, Form 2B

Write the letter for the correct answer in the blank at the right of each question.

For Questions 1–3, use ⊙D.

1. Name a radius.

   A. $\overline{AB}$ **C.** $\overline{CB}$

   B. $\overline{DB}$ **D.** $\overleftrightarrow{CE}$

1. _____

2. Name a chord that is not a diameter.

   F. $\overline{AB}$ **G.** $\overline{DB}$ **H.** $\overline{CB}$ **J.** $\overline{CE}$

2. _____

3. Name a secant.

   A. $\overline{AB}$ **B.** $\overline{DB}$ **C.** $\overleftrightarrow{CB}$ **D.** $\overleftrightarrow{CE}$

3. _____

4. The circumference of a steering wheel of a car is 20π inches. What is the radius of the steering wheel?

   F. 10 in.   **G.** 20 in.   **H.** 40 in.   **J.** 100 in.

4. _____

5. Find $m\widehat{GH}$.

   A. 20°   **C.** 70°

   B. 50°   **D.** 90°

5. _____

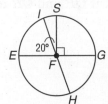

6. Points G and H lie on ⊙T so that $TH = 8$ meters and $m\angle GTH = 45$. Find the length of $\widehat{GH}$ to the nearest hundredth.

   F. 6.28 m   **G.** 12.57 m   **H.** 25.13 m   **J.** 37.70 m

6. _____

7. In ⊙X, chords $\overline{AB}$ and $\overline{CD}$ are congruent and $\overline{AB}$ is 9 units from X. Find the distance from $\overline{CD}$ to X.

   A. 4.5 units   **B.** 9 units   **C.** 18 units   **D.** cannot tell

7. _____

8. Detrmine the radius of ⊙O.

   F. $4\sqrt{2}$ units   **H.** $4\sqrt{3}$ units

   G. 8 units   **J.** $4\sqrt{2} + 4$ units

8. _____

9. Find x.

   A. 36   **C.** 144

   B. 72   **D.** 180

9. _____

10. Triangle JKL is inscribed in ⊙P with diameter $\overline{JK}$ and $m\widehat{JL} = 130$. Find $m\angle KJL$.

   F. 25   **G.** 50   **H.** 65   **J.** 130

10. _____

11. The measure of an angle formed by two tangents to a circle is 90°. If the radius of the circle is 8 centimeters, how far is the vertex of the angle from the center of the circle?

   A. 8 cm   **B.** $8\sqrt{2}$ cm   **C.** $8\sqrt{3}$ cm   **D.** 16 cm

11. _____

12. If $\overline{DE}$, $\overline{EF}$, and $\overline{FD}$ are tangent to $\odot A$, find EF.

    F. 9 ft   **H.** 7 ft

    G. 8 ft   **J.** 6 ft

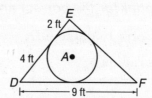

12. _____

13. Circle A has its center at $A(5, 7)$ and $\overleftrightarrow{CB}$ is tangent to $\odot A$ at $B(2, 8)$. Find the slope of $\overleftrightarrow{CB}$.

    A. 3   **B.** $\frac{1}{3}$ **C.** $-\frac{1}{3}$ **D.** -3

13. _____

14. If $\overleftrightarrow{AB}$ is tangent to $\odot P$ at B, find $m\angle 1$.

    F. 43   **H.** 137

    G. 86   **J.** 274

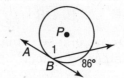

14. _____

15. Find $m\angle PQR$ if $\overrightarrow{QP}$ and $\overrightarrow{QR}$ are tangent to $\odot X$.

    A. 70   **C.** 125

    B. 110   **D.** 140

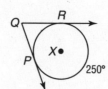

15. _____

16. Find x.

    F. $\frac{15}{7}$ **H.** 9

    G. 5   **J.** $\frac{35}{3}$

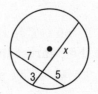

16. _____

17. Find y.

    A. 7   **C.** $\frac{59}{5}$

    B. $\frac{48}{5}$ **D.** $\frac{288}{25}$

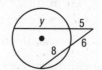

17. _____

18. Find the center of the circle whose equation is $(x + 15)^2 + (y - 20)^2 = 100$.

    F. $(-15, -20)$ **G.** $(15, -20)$ **H.** $(15, 20)$ **J.** $(-15, 20)$

18. _____

19. Find the equation of a circle whose center is at $(-1, 5)$ and radius is 8.

    A. $(x - 1)^2 + (y + 5)^2 = 8$ **C.** $(x + 1)^2 + (y - 5)^2 = 8$

    B. $(x - 1)^2 + (y + 5)^2 = 64$ **D.** $(x + 1)^2 + (y - 5)^2 = 64$

19. _____

20. Find the equation of $\odot P$.

    F. $(x + 4)^2 + (y - 2)^2 = 3$

    G. $(x + 4)^2 + (y - 2)^2 = 9$

    H. $(x - 4)^2 + (y + 2)^2 = 3$

    J. $(x - 4)^2 + (y + 2)^2 = 9$

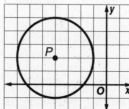

20. _____

Bonus Is the point $(-3, -5)$ inside, outside, or on the circle whose equation is $(x + 7)^2 + (y - 2)^2 = 62$?

    B: _____

10   Chapter 10 Test, Form 2C

1. Find *YB* if the diameter of ⊙*A* is 10 inches, the diameter of ⊙*B* is 8 inches, and *AX* = 3 inches.

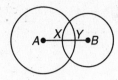

1. _____

2. Find the radius and diameter of a frisbee with a circumference of 11π inches.

2. _____

3. In ⊙*K*, $m\angle HKG = x + 10$ and $m\angle IKJ = 3x - 22$. Find $m\widehat{FJ}$.

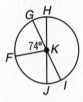

3. _____

4. The diameter of ⊙*C* is 18 units long. Find the length of an arc that has a measure of 100. Round to the nearest hundredth.

4. _____

5. In ⊙*A*, $CG = 5x + 2$ and $GD = 7x - 12$. Find *x*.

5. _____

6. In ⊙*O*, *PQ* = 18 meters. Find the distance from *O* to $\overline{PQ}$.

6. _____

7. Find *x*.

7. _____

8. A regular decagon is inscribed in a circle. Find the measure of each minor arc.

8. _____

9. $\overleftrightarrow{CD}$ is tangent to ⊙*Z* at (1, 7). If *Z* has coordinates (5, 2), find the slope of $\overleftrightarrow{CD}$.

9. _____

10. Triangle *DEF* is circumscribed about ⊙*O* with *DE* = 15 units, *DF* = 12 units, and *EF* = 13 units. Find the length of each segment whose endpoints are *D* and the points of tangency on $\overline{DE}$ and $\overline{DF}$.

10. _____

11. Find *x*.

11. _____

12. Find x if $\overrightarrow{BA}$ is tangent to $\odot P$ at A.

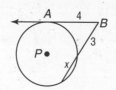

12. _____

For Questions 13–16, use $\odot G$ with $\overrightarrow{FA}$ and $\overrightarrow{FE}$ tangent at A and E.

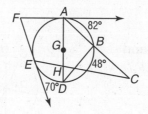

13. Find $m\angle ACE$.

13. _____

14. Find $m\angle ADB$.

14. _____

15. Find $m\angle AFE$.

15. _____

16. Find $m\angle EHD$.

16. _____

17. Determine the radius of a circle with an equation of $(x - 3)^2 + (y - 2)^2 = r^2$ and containing $(1, 4)$.

17. _____

18. Write the equation of a circle with a diameter having endpoints at $(-2, 6)$ and $(8, 4)$.

18. _____

19. Write the equation of a circle with a radius of 10 and a center at $(-4, -9)$.

19. _____

20. Graph $(x + 1)^2 + (y - 2)^2 = 16$.

20.

Bonus $\overleftrightarrow{AB}$ is tangent to $\odot P$ at $(5, 1)$. The equation for $\odot P$ is $x^2 + y^2 - 2x + 4y = 20$. Write the equation of $\overleftrightarrow{AB}$ in slope-intercept form.

B: _____

10 **Chapter 10 Test, Form 2D**

1. Find *AB*.

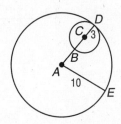

1. _____

2. Jon wants to put a circular decorative glass in a table. He cuts a hole in the table with a circular saw using a blade that is 20 inches in diameter. To place the glass in the table, he uses a thin metal frame along the edge of the hole. What is the length of the frame?

2. _____

3. In $\odot L$, $m\angle QLN = 2x - 5$. Find x.

3. _____

4. The radius of $\odot C$ is 16 units long. Find the length of an arc that has a measure of 270. Round to the nearest hundredth.

4. _____

5. If $\overline{DE}$ bisects $\overline{AB}$, what is the measure of $\angle BCE$?

5. _____

6. Find the radius of $\odot O$ if $XY = 10$.

6. _____

7. Find x.

7. _____

8. Regular nonagon *ABCDEFGHI* is inscribed in a circle. Find $m\widehat{AC}$.

8. _____

9. $\overleftrightarrow{EF}$ is tangent to circle P at $G(3, 6)$. If the slope of $\overleftrightarrow{EF}$ is $\frac{5}{3}$, what is the slope of $\overline{GP}$?

9. _____

10. Triangle *GHI* is circumscribed about $\odot K$ with $GH = 20$ units, $HI = 14$ units, and $IG = 12$ units. Find the length of each segment whose endpoints are G and the points of tangency on $\overline{GH}$ and $\overline{GI}$.

10. _____

11. Find x.

11. _____

10 **Chapter 10 Test, Form 2D** *(continued)*

12. Find x.

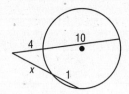

12. _____

For Questions 13–16, use $\odot O$ with $\triangle PQR$ circumscribed.

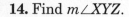

13. Find $m\angle PQR$.

13. _____

14. Find $m\angle XYZ$.

14. _____

15. Find $m\angle PYX$.

15. _____

16. Find $m\angle XUZ$.

16. _____

17. Write the equation of the circle with its center at $(-7, 8)$ and radius of 9.

17. _____

18. Write the equation of the circle containing the point $(8, 1)$ and a center at $(4, -9)$.

18. _____

19. Find the radius of a circle with an equation of $(x + 3)^2 + (y - 2)^2 = r^2$ and containing $(0, 8)$.

19. _____

20. Graph $(x - 3)^2 + (y + 1)^2 = 25$.

20.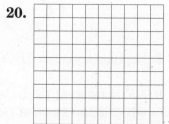

Bonus Find the coordinates of the point(s) of intersection of the circles whose equations are $(x - 2)^2 + y^2 = 13$ and $(x + 3)^2 + y^2 = 8$.

B: _____

10 Chapter 10 Test, Form 3

1. Find BC.

1. _____

2. Find the circumference of $\odot P$ to the nearest hundredth.

2. _____

3. Find $m\widehat{XW}$.

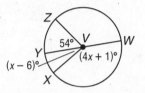

3. _____

4. If the length of an arc of measure 80 is 12π inches, find the radius of the circle.

4. _____

5. Find GH.

5. _____

6. Two parallel chords 16 centimeters and 30 centimeters long are 23 centimeters apart. Find the radius of the circle.

6. _____

7. Find x.

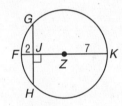

7. _____

8. The four corners of a square chessboard touch the edge of a round table. The length of the chessboard is 1 foot. Find the radius of the table.

8. _____

9. In $\odot O$, $\overline{OA}$ and $\overline{OB}$ are radii and $m\angle BOA = 120$. Tangents $\overline{PA}$ and $\overline{PB}$ have length 10. Find OA.

9. _____

10. Quadrilateral $ABCD$ is circumscribed about $\odot O$. If $AB = 7$, $BC = 11$, and $DC = 8$, find AD.

10. _____

11. Find x.

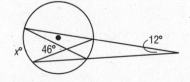

11. _____

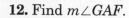

10 **Chapter 10 Test, Form 3** *(continued)*

For Questions 12–14, use ⊙D with
tangents $\overrightarrow{AS}$ and $\overrightarrow{AM}$.

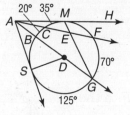

12. Find $m\angle GAF$.

13. Find $m\angle GMH$.

14. Find $m\angle AEM$.

15. Find BE.

12. _____

13. _____

14. _____

15. _____

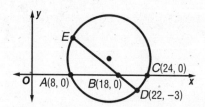

16. If $\overrightarrow{CD}$ is tangent to ⊙P, find x.

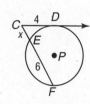

16. _____

17. Find the coordinates of the points of intersection of the line
$5x + 6y = 30$ and the circle $x^2 + y^2 = 25$.

17. _____

18. Write the equation of the circle whose center is at $(-3, -2)$
and that is tangent to the y-axis.

18. _____

19. Find the center and radius of the circle whose equation is
$x^2 - 12x + y^2 + 14y + 4 = 0$.

19. _____

20. Graph $x^2 + (y + 6)^2 = 1$.

20.

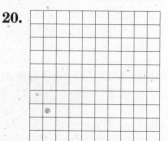

Bonus Find the coordinates of the center of the circle containing
the points $(0, 0)$, $(-2, 4)$, and $(4, -2)$.

B: _____

Demonstrate your knowledge by giving a clear, concise solution to each problem. Be sure to include all relevant drawings and justify your answers. You may show your solution in more than one way or investigate beyond the requirements of the problem.

1. Make up a set of data, perhaps modeling a survey, that you can represent with a circle graph. Calculate the number of degrees for each sector. Draw and label the circle graph. You must have at least four noncongruent sectors on your graph.

2. **a.** Explain the difference between the length of an arc and the measure of an arc.

   b. Is it possible for two arcs to have the same measure but different lengths? Explain your answer.

3. Use a compass to construct a circle. Label the center P. Then draw two chords that are not diameters of $\odot P$. Locate the center of your circle by constructing the perpendicular bisectors of these two chords.

4. An inscribed regular polygon intercepts congruent arcs on the circle. What happens to the measures of these arcs as you increase the number of sides of the polygon?

5. **a.** Write an equation of a circle whose center is not at $(0, 0)$. Write your equation in $(x - h)^2 + (y - k)^2 = r^2$ form.

   b. Find the coordinates of any point B that lies on the circle.

   c. Write an equation of the line through point B that is tangent to the circle. Write your equation in $y = mx + b$ form.

10 Standardized Test Practice (Chapters 1–10)

Part 1: Multiple Choice

Instructions: Fill in the appropriate circle for the best answer.

1. Find the slope of a segment with endpoints at $(2a, -b)$ and $(-a, -3b)$. (Lesson 3-6)

A $\dfrac{-a}{4b}$ **B** $\dfrac{3a}{2b}$ **C** $\dfrac{2b}{3a}$ **D** $\dfrac{-4b}{a}$

1. Ⓐ Ⓑ Ⓒ Ⓓ

2. If $\overline{PT}$ and $\overline{QS}$ are medians of $\triangle PQR$, which term describes M? (Lesson 5-1)

F incenter   **H** orthocenter
G centroid   **J** segment bisector

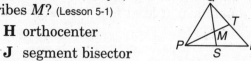

2. Ⓕ Ⓖ Ⓗ Ⓙ

3. If $\overline{DE}$ is an angle bisector of $\angle GDH$, which is a true statement? (Lesson 6-5)

A $\dfrac{a}{b} = \dfrac{y}{x}$

B $\dfrac{a}{b} = \dfrac{x}{y}$

C $(a + b)^2 = x^2 + y^2$

D $DE = DH$

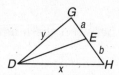

3. Ⓐ Ⓑ Ⓒ Ⓓ

4. A plane flies at an altitude of 350 meters and then starts to descend when it is 6 kilometers from the runway. What is the angle of depression for the descent of the plane? (Lesson 7-5)

F about 3.3°   **G** about 33.4°   **H** about 8.9°   **J** about 89°

4. Ⓕ Ⓖ Ⓗ Ⓙ

5. Which statement is *not* true for all rectangles? (Lesson 8-4)

A The diagonals are congruent and bisect each other.
B Opposite sides are congruent and parallel.
C The diagonals are perpendicular.
D Opposite angles are congruent.

5. Ⓐ Ⓑ Ⓒ Ⓓ

6. What transformation relates $\triangle CDF$ and $\triangle C'D'F'$? (Lesson 9-2)

F reflection   **H** rotation
G translation   **J** dilation

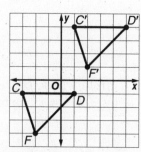

6. Ⓕ Ⓖ Ⓗ Ⓙ

7. Which is a true statement if $\overline{XY}$ is tangent to $\odot P$? (Lesson 10-7)

A $ab = bc$ **B** $a = bc$
C $a^2 = bc$ **D** $a^2 = b(b + c)$

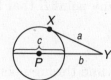

7. Ⓐ Ⓑ Ⓒ Ⓓ

10 Standardized Test Practice *(continued)*

8. Toby Toy Company sells an average of 560 toys over the Internet each week. There are presently 8500 toys in stock. Which describes how many toys they will have in stock after x weeks if no new toys are added? (Lesson 3-4)

8.

   F $y = -560x + 8500$

   G $y = 560x + 8500$

   H $y = -8500x + 560$

   J $y = 8500x + 560$

9. Find the value of x. (Lesson 4-6)

9. Ⓐ Ⓑ Ⓒ Ⓓ

   A 105   **C** 129.5

   B 111   **D** 138

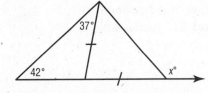

10. Which assumption would you make to start an indirect proof of the statement *If $3a - 4 < 11$, then $a < 5$.* (Lesson 5-3)

10. Ⓕ Ⓖ Ⓗ Ⓙ

    F $a \leq 5$ **G** $a \geq 5$ **H** $a \neq 5$ **J** $a = 5$

11. Find the image of $\overline{AB}$ with $A(-4, 2)$ and $B(-2, 4)$ under a rotation of 90° counterclockwise about the origin. (Lesson 9-3)

11. Ⓐ Ⓑ Ⓒ Ⓓ

    A $A'(-2, 4), B'(-4, 2)$ **C** $A'(-2, 4), B'(4, 2)$

    B $A'(4, -2), B'(2, -4)$ **D** $A'(4, 2), B'(2, 4)$

Part 2: Griddable

Instructions: Enter your answer by writing each digit of the answer in a column box and then shading in the appropriate circle that corresponds to that entry.

12. If *ABCD* is an isosceles trapezoid with bases $\overline{BC}$ and $\overline{AD}$, median $\overline{EF}$, $EF = 43$, and $BC = 12$, find AD. (Lesson 8-6)

12.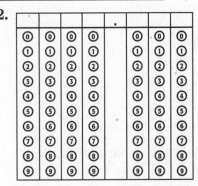

13. Find $m\angle 5$. (Lesson 10-6)

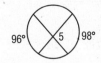

13.

Part 3: Short Response

Instructions: Write your answer in the space provided.

14. Two parallel lines are cut by a transversal so that $\angle 1$ and $\angle 2$ are alternate interior angles. Find $m\angle 1$ if $m\angle 1 = 3y - 5$ and $m\angle 2 = y + 7$. (Lesson 3-2)

14. _____

15. Determine the relationship between the lengths of $\overline{AB}$ and $\overline{BC}$. (Lesson 5-2)

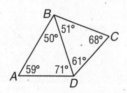

15. _____

16. Determine whether $\triangle GHJ$ is a right triangle given $G(3, 7)$, $H(-2, 5)$, and $J(-4, 10)$. (Lesson 7-2)

16. _____

17. If $\overline{CD}$ is tangent to $\odot P$, find a. (Lesson 10-5)

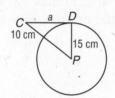

17. _____

18. If p is true and q is false, find the truth value of $p \wedge \sim q$. (Lesson 2-2)

18. _____

19. Write a similarity statement. (Lesson 6-2)

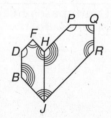

19. _____

20. If $WXYZ$ is a parallelogram, find a and b. (Lesson 8-3)

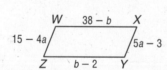

20. _____

21. For the circle with center at $(4, -1)$ and a diameter of 24: (Lesson 10-8)

   a. Write an equation that represents this circle.

21. a. _____

   b. Find the circumference of the circle.

21. b. _____

   c. Find the area of the circle.

21. c. _____

NAME _____ DATE _____ PERIOD _____

10 Anticipation Guide

Circles and Circumference

Step 1 **Before you begin Chapter 10**

- Read each statement.
- Decide whether you Agree (A) or Disagree (D) with the statement.
- Write A or D in the first column OR if you are not sure whether you agree or disagree, write NS (Not Sure).

STEP 1 A, D, or NS		Statement	STEP 2 A or D
	1.	The distance from any point on a circle to the center of the circle is called the diameter.	D
	2.	A chord of a circle is any segment with endpoints that are on the circle.	A
	3.	The formula for the circumference of a circle is $C = \pi r^2$.	D
	4.	The vertex of a central angle of a circle is at the center of the circle.	A
	5.	If two arcs from two different circles have the same measure then the arcs are congruent.	D
	6.	In a circle, two minor arcs are congruent if their corresponding chords are congruent.	A
	7.	In a circle, two chords are equidistant from the center are congruent.	A
	8.	The measure of an inscribed angle equals the measure of its intercepted arc.	D
	9.	A line is tangent to a circle only if it contains a chord of the circle.	D
	10.	Two secant lines of a circle can intersect in the interior or the exterior of the circle.	A
	11.	If two chords intersect inside a circle then the two chords are congruent.	D
	12.	The center of a circle represented by the equation $(x + 3)^2 + (y + 5)^2 = 9$ is located at (3, 5).	D

Step 2 *After you complete Chapter 10*

- Reread each statement and complete the last column by entering an A or a D.
- Did any of your opinions about the statements change from the first column?
- For those statements that you mark with a D, use a piece of paper to write an example of why you disagree.

Chapter 10

3

Glencoe Geometry

10-1 Lesson Reading Guide

Circles and Circumference

Get Ready for the Lesson

Read the introduction to Lesson 10-1 in your textbook.

How could you measure the approximate distance around the circular carousel using everyday measuring devices? **Sample answer: Place a piece of string along the rim of the carousel. Cut off a length of string that covers the perimeter of the circle. Straighten the string and measure it with a yardstick.**

Read the Lesson

1. Refer to the figure.

a. Name the circle. $\odot Q$

b. Name four radii of the circle. $\overline{QP}, \overline{QR}, \overline{QS},$ and $\overline{QT}$

c. Name a diameter of the circle. $\overline{PR}$

d. Name two chords of the circle. $\overline{PR}$ and $\overline{ST}$

2. Match each description from the first column with the best term from the second column. (Some terms in the second column may be used more than once or not at all.)

a. a segment other than the diameter endpoints on a circle **iii**

b. the set of all points in a plane that are the same distance from a given point **iv**

c. the distance between the center of a circle and any point on the circle **i**

d. a chord that passes through the center of a circle **ii**

e. a segment whose endpoints are the center and any point on a circle **i**

f. a chord made up of two collinear radii **ii**

g. the distance around a circle **v**

   i. radius
   ii. diameter
   iii. chord
   iv. circle
   v. circumference

3. Which equations correctly express a relationship in a circle? **A, D, G**

A. $d = 2r$ B. $C = \pi r$ C. $C = 2d$ D. $d = \dfrac{C}{\pi}$

E. $r = \dfrac{d}{\pi}$ F. $C = r^2$ G. $C = 2\pi r$ H. $d = \dfrac{1}{2}r$

Remember What You Learned

4. A good way to remember a new geometric term is to relate the word or its parts to geometric terms you already know. Look up the origins of the two parts of the word *diameter* in your dictionary. Explain the meaning of each part and give a term you already know that shares the origin of that part. **Sample answer: The first part comes from *dia*, which means *across* or *through*, as in *diagonal*. The second part comes from *metron*, which means *measure*, as in *geometry*.**

Chapter 10

5

Glencoe Geometry

Answers

Left Page (page 6)

NAME _____ DATE _____ PERIOD _____

10-1 Study Guide and Intervention
Circles and Circumference

Parts of Circles A **circle** consists of all points in a plane that are a given distance, called the **radius**, from a given point called the **center**.

A segment or line can intersect a circle in several ways.

• A segment with endpoints that are the center of the circle and a point of the circle is a **radius**.

• A segment with endpoints that lie on the circle is a **chord**.

• A chord that contains the circle's center is a **diameter**.

chord: $\overline{AE}$, $\overline{BD}$
radius: $\overline{FB}$, $\overline{FC}$, $\overline{FD}$
diameter: $\overline{BD}$

Example Name the circle.

a. **Name the circle.**
The name of the circle is $\odot O$.

b. **Name radii of the circle.**
AO, BO, CO, and DO are radii.

c. **Name chords of the circle.**
AB and CD are chords.

d. **Name a diameter of the circle.**
AB is a diameter.

Exercises

1. Name the circle. $\odot R$

2. Name radii of the circle. $\overline{RA}$, $\overline{RB}$, $\overline{RY}$, and $\overline{RX}$

3. Name chords of the circle. $\overline{BY}$, $\overline{AX}$, $\overline{AB}$, and $\overline{XY}$

4. Name diameters of the circle. $\overline{AB}$ and $\overline{XY}$

5. Find AR if AB is 18 millimeters. 9 mm

6. Find AR and AB if RY is 10 inches. $AR = 10$ in.; $AB = 20$ in.

7. Is $\overline{AB} \cong \overline{XY}$? Explain. **Yes;** all diameters of the same circle are congruent.

Chapter 10   6   Glencoe Geometry

Right Page (page 7)

NAME _____ DATE _____ PERIOD _____

10-1 Study Guide and Intervention (continued)
Circles and Circumference

Circumference The **circumference** of a circle is the distance around the circle.

Circumference	For a circumference of C units and a diameter of d units or a radius of r units, $C = \pi d$ or $C = 2\pi r$.

13 cm

Example Find the circumference of the circle to the nearest hundredth.

$C = 2\pi r$ Circumference formula
$= 2\pi(13)$ $r = 13$
≈ 81.68 Use a calculator.

The circumference is about 81.68 centimeters.

Exercises

Find the circumference of a circle with the given radius or diameter. Round to the nearest hundredth.

1. $r = 8$ cm   50.27 cm

2. $r = 3\sqrt{2}$ ft   26.66 ft

3. $r = 4.1$ cm   25.76 cm

4. $d = 10$ in.   31.42 in.

5. $d = \frac{1}{3}$ m   1.05 m

6. $d = 18$ yd   56.55 yd

The radius, diameter, or circumference of a circle is given. Find the missing measures to the nearest hundredth.

7. $r = 4$ cm $d = $ __8 cm__ , $C = $ __25.13 cm__

8. $d = 6$ ft $r = $ __3 ft__ , $C = $ __18.85 ft__

9. $r = 12$ cm $d = $ __24 cm__ , $C = $ __75.40 cm__

10. $d = 15$ in. $r = $ __7.5 in.__ , $C = $ __47.12 in.__

Find the exact circumference of each circle.

11.

5 cm, 12 cm   13π cm

12. 2π cm

$\sqrt{2}$ cm, $\sqrt{2}$ cm

Chapter 10   7   Glencoe Geometry

Skills Practice Page (10-1)

NAME _____ DATE _____ PERIOD _____

10-1 Skills Practice

Circles and Circumference

For Exercises 1–5, refer to the circle at the right.

1. Name the circle. ⊙P

2. Name a radius. $\overline{PA}$, $\overline{PB}$, or $\overline{PC}$

3. Name a chord. $\overline{AB}$ or $\overline{DE}$

4. Name a diameter. $\overline{AB}$

5. Name a radius not drawn as part of a diameter. $\overline{PC}$

6. Suppose the diameter of the circle is 16 centimeters. Find the radius. 8 cm

7. If $PC = 11$ inches, find AB. 22 in.

The diameters of ⊙F and ⊙G are 5 and 6 units, respectively. Find each measure.

8. BF 0.5

9. AB 2

The radius, diameter, or circumference of a circle is given. Find the missing measures to the nearest hundredth.

10. $r = 8$ cm $d = $ 16 cm , $C \approx$ 50.27 cm

11. $r = 13$ ft $d = $ 26 ft , $C \approx$ 81.68 ft

12. $d = 9$ m $r = $ 4.5 m , $C \approx$ 28.27 m

13. $C = 35.7$ in. $d \approx$ 11.36 in. , $r \approx$ 5.68 in.

Find the exact circumference of each circle.

14. $3\pi\sqrt{2}$ cm

15. 17π ft

Chapter 10   8   *Glencoe Geometry*

Practice Page (10-1)

NAME _____ DATE _____ PERIOD _____

10-1 Practice

Circles and Circumference

For Exercises 1–7, refer to the circle at the right.

1. Name the circle. ⊙L

2. Name a radius. $\overline{LR}$, $\overline{LT}$, or $\overline{LW}$

3. Name a chord. $\overline{RT}$, $\overline{RS}$, or $\overline{ST}$

4. Name a diameter. $\overline{RT}$

5. Name a radius not drawn as part of a diameter. $\overline{LW}$

6. Suppose the radius of the circle is 3.5 yards. Find the diameter. 7 yd

7. If $RT = 19$ meters, find LW. 9.5 m

The diameters of ⊙L and ⊙M are 20 and 13 units, respectively. Find each measure if $QR = 4$.

8. LQ 6

9. RM 2.5

The radius, diameter, or circumference of a circle is given. Find the missing measures to the nearest hundredth.

10. $r = 7.5$ mm $d = $ 15 mm , $C \approx$ 47.12 mm

11. $C = 227.6$ yd $d \approx$ 72.45 yd , $r \approx$ 36.22 yd

Find the exact circumference of each circle.

12. 25π cm

13. 58π mi

SUNDIALS For Exercises 14 and 15, use the following information.
Herman purchased a sundial to use as the centerpiece for a garden. The diameter of the sundial is 9.5 inches.

14. Find the radius of the sundial. 4.75 in.

15. Find the circumference of the sundial to the nearest hundredth. 29.85 in.

Chapter 10   9   *Glencoe Geometry*

Answers (Lesson 10–1)

10-1 Enrichment

Sectors

The area of a circle is found by using the formula $A = \pi r^2$. A sector is a pie-shaped portion of the circle enclosed by 2 radii and the edge of the circle. A central angle of a sector is an angle whose vertex is at the center of the circle and crosses the circle.

The area of a circle is represented by the formula $A = \pi r^2$. The area of the sector θ is proportional to the part that the central angle is of 360°.

$$\frac{\text{area of sector}}{\text{area of the circle}} = \frac{\theta}{360} \quad \text{or area of sector} = \frac{\theta}{360}\,\pi r^2.$$

Example Find the area of the sector shown at the right.

$A = \dfrac{\theta}{360}\,\pi r^2$

$A = \dfrac{90}{360}\,\pi 2^2 \quad r = 2,\ \theta = 90$

$= \dfrac{1}{4}(4\pi) \text{ or } \pi$

So the area of the sector is π in² or approximately 3.14 square inches.

Exercises

1. Find the area of a sector if the circle has a radius of 10 centimeters and the central angle measures 72°.
   20π cm²

2. Find the area of a sector if the circle has a radius of 5 inches and the central angle measures 60°.
   $\dfrac{25}{6}\pi$ in²

3. If the area of a sector is 15π square centimeters and the radius of the circle is 5 centimeters, find the measure of the central angle. **216**

4. Find the measure of the central angle that intercepts a sector that is $\dfrac{1}{3}$ the area of the circle.
   120

10-1 Word Problem Practice

Circles and Circumference

1. **WHEELS** Zack is designing wheels for a concept car. The diameter of the wheel is 18 inches. Zack wants to make spokes in the wheel that run from the center of the wheel to the rim. In other words, each spoke is a radius of the wheel. How long are these spokes?
   9 in.

2. **CAKE CUTTING** Kathy slices through a circular cake. The cake has a diameter of 14 inches. The slice that Kathy made is straight and has a length of 11 inches.

   Did Kathy cut along a *radius*, a *diameter*, or a *chord* of the circle?
   chord

3. **COINS** Three identical circular coins are lined up in a row as shown.

   The distance between the centers of the first and third coins is 3.2 centimeters. What is the radius of one of these coins?
   0.8 cm

4. **PLAZAS** A rectangular plaza has a surrounding circular fence. The diagonals of the rectangle pass from one point on the fence through the center of the circle to another point on the fence.

   Based on the information in the figure, what is the diameter of the fence? Round your answer to the nearest tenth of a foot.
   449.6 ft

EXERCISE HOOPS For Exercises 5 and 6, use the following information.
Taiga wants to make a circular loop that he can twirl around his body for exercise. He will use a tube that is 2.5 meters long.

5. What will be the diameter of Taiga's exercise hoop? Round your answer to the nearest thousandth of a meter.
   0.796 m

6. What will be the radius of Taiga's exercise hoop? Round your answer to the nearest thousandth of a meter.
   0.398 m

NAME _____ DATE _____ PERIOD _____

10-2 Study Guide and Intervention

Measuring Angles and Arcs

Angles and Arcs A **central angle** is an angle whose vertex is at the center of a circle and whose sides are radii. A central angle separates a circle into two arcs, a **major arc** and a **minor arc**.

Here are some properties of central angles and arcs.
- The sum of the measures of the central angles of a circle with no interior points in common is 360.
- The measure of a minor arc equals the measure of its central angle.
- The measure of a major arc is 360 minus the measure of the minor arc.
- Two arcs are congruent if and only if their corresponding central angles are congruent.
- The measure of an arc formed by two adjacent arcs is the sum of the measures of the two arcs. **(Arc Addition Postulate)**

GF is a minor arc.
CHG is a major arc.
$\angle GEF$ is a central angle.

$m\angle HEC + m\angle CEF + m\angle FEG + m\angle GEH = 360$

$m\widehat{CF} = m\angle CEF$

$m\widehat{CGF} = 360 - m\widehat{CF}$

$\widehat{CF} \cong \widehat{FG}$ if and only if $\angle CEF \cong \angle FEG$.

$m\widehat{CF} + m\widehat{FG} = m\widehat{CG}$

Example In $\odot R$, $m\angle ARB = 42$ and $\overline{AC}$ is a diameter. Find $m\widehat{AB}$ and $m\widehat{ACB}$.

$\angle ARB$ is a central angle and $m\angle ARB = 42$, so $m\widehat{AB} = 42$.
Thus $m\widehat{ACB} = 360 - 42$ or 318.

Exercises

Find each measure.

1. $m\angle SCT$ **75**

2. $m\angle SCU$ **135**

3. $m\angle SCQ$ **90**

4. $m\angle QCT$ **165**

In $\odot O$, $m\angle BOA = 44$. Find each measure.

5. $m\widehat{BA}$ **44**

6. $m\widehat{BC}$ **136**

7. $m\widehat{CD}$ **44**

8. $m\widehat{ACB}$ **316**

9. $m\widehat{BCD}$ **180**

10. $m\widehat{AD}$ **136**

Chapter 10   13   *Glencoe Geometry*

NAME _____ DATE _____ PERIOD _____

10-2 Lesson Reading Guide

Measuring Angles and Arcs

Get Ready for the Lesson

Read the introduction to Lesson 10-2 in your textbook.

- What is the measure of the angle formed by the hour hand and the minute hand of the clock at 5:00? **150**

- What is the measure of the angle formed by the hour hand and the minute hand at 10:30? (Hint: How has each hand moved since 10:00?) **135**

Read the Lesson

1. Refer to $\odot P$. $\overline{AC}$ is a diameter. Indicate whether each statement is *true* or *false*.

a. $\widehat{DAB}$ is a major arc. **false**

b. $\widehat{ADC}$ is a semicircle. **true**

c. $\widehat{AD} \cong \widehat{CD}$ **true**

d. $\widehat{DA}$ and $\widehat{AB}$ are adjacent arcs. **true**

e. $\angle BPC$ is an acute central angle. **false**

f. $\angle DPA$ and $\angle BPA$ are supplementary central angles. **false**

2. Refer to the figure in Exercise 1. Give each of the following arc measures.

a. $m\widehat{AB}$ **52**

b. $m\widehat{CD}$ **90**

c. $m\widehat{BC}$ **128**

d. $m\widehat{ADC}$ **180**

e. $m\widehat{DAB}$ **142**

f. $m\widehat{DCB}$ **218**

g. $m\widehat{DAC}$ **270**

h. $m\widehat{BDA}$ **308**

3. Underline the correct word or number to form a true statement.

a. The arc measure of a semicircle is (90/180/360).

b. Arcs of a circle that have exactly one point in common are (congruent/opposite/adjacent) arcs.

c. The measure of a major arc is greater than (0/90/180) and less than (90/180/360). If the

d. Suppose a set of central angles of a circle have interiors that do not overlap. If the angles and their interiors contain all points of the circle, then the sum of the measures of the central angles is (90/270/360).

e. The measure of an arc formed by two adjacent arcs is the (sum/difference/product) of the measures of the two arcs.

f. The measure of a minor arc is greater than (0/90/180) and less than (90/180/360).

Remember What You Learned

4. A good way to remember something is to explain it to someone else. Suppose your classmate Luis does not like to work with proportions. What is a way that he can find the length of a minor arc of a circle without solving a proportion? **Sample answer: Divide the measure of the central angle of the arc by 360 to form a fraction. Multiply this fraction by the circumference of the circle to find the length of the arc.**

Chapter 10   12   *Glencoe Geometry*

Answers

Lesson 10-2

10-2 Skills Practice

Measuring Angles and Arcs

ALGEBRA In $\odot R$, $\overline{AC}$ and $\overline{EB}$ are diameters. Find each measure.

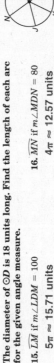

1. $m\angle ERD$ 28
2. $m\angle CRD$ 108
3. $m\angle BRC$ 44
4. $m\angle ARB$ 136
5. $m\angle ARE$ 44
6. $m\angle BPD$ 152

In $\odot A$, $m\angle PAU = 40$, $\angle PAU \cong \angle SAT$, and $\angle RAS \cong \angle TAU$. Find each measure.

7. $m\widehat{PQ}$ 90
8. $m\widehat{PQR}$ 180
9. $m\widehat{ST}$ 40
10. $m\widehat{RS}$ 50
11. $m\widehat{RSU}$ 140
12. $m\widehat{STP}$ 130
13. $m\widehat{PQS}$ 230
14. $m\widehat{PRU}$ 320

The diameter of $\odot D$ is 18 units long. Find the length of each arc for the given angle measure.

15. $\widehat{LM}$ if $m\angle LDM = 100$ $5\pi \approx 15.71$ units
16. $\widehat{MN}$ if $m\angle MDN = 80$ $4\pi \approx 12.57$ units
17. $\widehat{KL}$ if $m\angle KDL = 60$ $3\pi \approx 9.42$ units
18. $\widehat{NJK}$ if $m\angle NDK = 120$ $6\pi \approx 18.85$ units
19. $\widehat{KLM}$ if $m\angle KDM = 160$ $8\pi \approx 25.13$ units
20. $\widehat{JK}$ if $m\angle JDK = 50$ $2.5\pi \approx 7.85$ units

Chapter 10   15   *Glencoe Geometry*

10-2 Study Guide and Intervention *(continued)*

Measuring Angles and Arcs

Arc Length An arc is part of a circle and its length is a part of the circumference of the circle.

Example In $\odot R$, $m\angle ARB = 135$, $RB = 8$, and AC is a diameter. Find the length of $\overline{AB}$.

$m\angle ARB = 135$, so $m\widehat{AB} = 135$. Using the formula $C = 2\pi r$, the circumference is $2\pi(8)$ or 16π. To find the length of AB, write a proportion to compare each part to its whole.

$$\frac{\text{length of } AB}{\text{circumference}} = \frac{\text{degree measure of arc}}{\text{degree measure of circle}} \quad \text{Proportion}$$

$$\frac{\ell}{16\pi} = \frac{135}{360} \quad \text{Substitution}$$

$$\ell = \frac{(16\pi)(135)}{360} \quad \text{Multiply each side by } 16\pi.$$

$$= 6\pi \quad \text{Simplify.}$$

The length of AB is 6π or about 18.85 units.

Exercises

The diameter of $\odot O$ is 24 units long. Find the length of each arc for the given angle measure. Round to the nearest tenth.

1. $\widehat{DE}$ if $m\angle DOE = 120$ 8π or 25.1
2. $\widehat{DEA}$ if $m\angle DOE = 120$ 14π or 44.0
3. $\widehat{BC}$ if $m\angle COB = 45$ 3π or 9.4
4. $\widehat{CBA}$ if $m\angle COB = 45$ 9π or 28.3

The diameter of $\odot P$ is 15 units long and $\angle SPT \cong \angle RPT$. Find the length of each arc for the given angle measure. Round to the nearest tenth.

5. $\widehat{RT}$ if $m\angle SPT = 70$ $\frac{35}{12}\pi$ or 9.2
6. $\widehat{NR}$ if $m\angle RPT = 50$ $\frac{10}{3}\pi$ or 10.5
7. $\widehat{MST}$ 7.5π or 23.6
8. $\widehat{MRS}$ if $m\angle MPS = 140$ $\frac{55}{6}\pi$ or 28.8

Chapter 10   14   *Glencoe Geometry*

NAME _____ DATE _____ PERIOD _____

10-2 Practice

Measuring Angles and Arcs

ALGEBRA In ⊙Q, $\overline{AC}$ and $\overline{BD}$ are diameters. Find each measure.

1. $m\angle AQE$ **59**

2. $m\angle DQE$ **48**

3. $m\angle CQD$ **73**

4. $m\angle BQC$ **107**

5. $m\angle CQE$ **121**

6. $m\angle AQD$ **107**

In ⊙P, $m\angle GPH = 38$. Find each measure.

7. $m\widehat{EF}$ **38**

8. $m\widehat{DE}$ **52**

9. $m\widehat{FG}$ **142**

10. $m\widehat{DHG}$ **128**

11. $m\widehat{DFG}$ **232**

12. $m\widehat{DGE}$ **308**

The radius of ⊙Z is 13.5 units long. Find the length of each arc for the given angle measure.

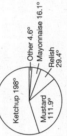

13. $\widehat{QPT}$ if $m\angle QZT = 120$
   $9\pi \approx 28.27$ units

14. $\widehat{QR}$ if $m\angle QZR = 60$
   $4.5\pi \approx 14.14$ units

15. $\widehat{PQR}$ if $m\angle PZR = 150$
   $11.25\pi \approx 35.34$ units

16. $\widehat{QPS}$ if $m\angle QZS = 160$
   $12\pi \approx 37.70$ units

HOMEWORK For Exercises 17 and 18, refer to the table, which shows the number of hours students at Leland High School say they spend on homework each night.

Homework	
Less than 1 hour	8%
1–2 hours	29%
2–3 hours	58%
3–4 hours	3%
Over 4 hours	2%

17. If you were to construct a circle graph of the data, how many degrees would be allotted to each category?
   28.8°, 104.4°, 208.8°, 10.8°, 7.2°

18. Describe the arcs associated with each category.
   The arc associated with 2–3 hours is a major arc; minor arcs are associated with the remaining categories.

NAME _____ DATE _____ PERIOD _____

10-2 Word Problem Practice

Measuring Angles and Arcs

1. **CONDIMENTS** A number of people in a park were asked to name their favorite condiment for hot dogs. The results are shown in the circle graph.

Ketchup 198°
Mustard 111.9°
Relish 29.4°
Mayonnaise 16.1°
Other 4.6°

What was the second most popular hot dog condiment?
mustard

2. **CLOCKS** Shiatsu is a Japanese massage technique. One of the beliefs is that various body functions are most active at various times during the day. To illustrate this, they use a Chinese clock that is based on a circle divided into 12 equal sections by radii.

What is the measure of any one of the 12 equal central angles?
30°

3. **PIES** Yolanda has divided a circular apple pie into 4 slices by cutting the pie along 4 radii. The central angles of the 4 slices are $3x$, $6x - 10$, $4x + 10$, and $5x$ degrees. What exactly are the numerical measures of the central angles?
60°, 110°, 90°, and 100°

4. **RIBBONS** Cora is wrapping a ribbon around a cylinder-shaped gift box. The box has a diameter of 15 inches and the ribbon is 60 inches long. Cora is able to wrap the ribbon all the way around the box once, and then continue so that the second end of the ribbon passes the first end. What is the central angle formed between the ends of the ribbon? Round your answer to the nearest tenth of a degree.
98.4°

BIKE WHEELS For Exercises 5–7, use the following information.
Lucy had to buy a new wheel for her bike. The bike wheel has a diameter of 20 inches.

5. If Lucy rolls the wheel one complete rotation along the ground, how far will the wheel travel? Round your answer to the nearest hundredth of an inch.
62.83 in.

6. If the bike wheel is rolled along the ground so that it rotates 45°, how far will the wheel travel? Round your answer to the nearest hundredth of an inch.
7.85 in.

7. If the bike wheel is rolled along the ground for 10 inches, through what angle does the wheel rotate? Round your answer to the nearest tenth of a degree.
57.3°

Answers

10-2 Enrichment

Curves of Constant Width

A circle is called a curve of constant width because no matter how you turn it, the greatest distance across it is always the same. However, the circle is not the only figure with this property.

The figure at the right is called a Reuleaux triangle.

1. Use a metric ruler to find the distance from P to any point on the opposite side. **4.6 cm**

2. Find the distance from Q to the opposite side. **4.6 cm**

3. What is the distance from R to the opposite side? **4.6 cm**

The Reuleaux triangle is made of three arcs. In the example shown, PQ has center R, QR has center P, and PR has center Q.

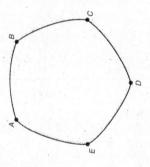

4. Trace the Reuleaux triangle above on a piece of paper and cut it out. Make a square with sides the length you found in Exercise 1. Show that you can turn the triangle inside the square while keeping its sides in contact with the sides of the square. **See students' work.**

5. Make a different curve of constant width by starting with the five points below and following the steps given.

Step 1: Place the point of your compass on D with opening DA. Make an arc with endpoints A and B.

Step 2: Make another arc from B to C that has center E.

Step 3: Continue this process until you have five arcs drawn.

Some countries use shapes like this for coins. They are useful because they can be distinguished by touch, yet they will work in vending machines because of their constant width.

6. Measure the width of the figure you made in Exercise 5. Draw two parallel lines with the distance between them equal to the width you found. On a piece of paper, trace the five-sided figure and cut it out. Show that it will roll between the lines drawn. **5.3 cm**

10-3 Lesson Reading Guide

Arcs and Chords

Get Ready for the Lesson

Read the introduction to Lesson 10-3 in your textbook.

What do you observe about any two of the grooves in the waffle iron shown in the picture in your textbook? **They are either parallel or perpendicular.**

Read the Lesson

1. Supply the missing words or phrases to form true statements.

   a. In a circle, if a radius is **perpendicular** to a chord, then it bisects the chord and its **arc**.

   b. In a circle or in **congruent** circles, two **minor arcs** are congruent if and only if their corresponding chords are congruent.

   c. In a circle or in **congruent** circles, two chords are congruent if they are **equidistant** from the center.

   d. A polygon is inscribed in a circle if all of its **vertices** lie on the circle.

   e. All of the sides of an inscribed polygon are **chords** of the circle.

2. If $\odot P$ has a diameter 40 centimeters long, and $AC = FD = 24$ centimeters, find each measure.

   a. PA **20 cm**   b. AG **12 cm**

   c. PE **20 cm**   d. PH **16 cm**

   e. HE **4 cm**   f. FG **36 cm**

3. In $\odot Q$, $RS = VW$ and $m\widehat{RS} = 70$. Find each measure.

   a. $m\widehat{RT}$ **35**   b. $m\widehat{ST}$ **35**

   c. $m\widehat{VW}$ **70**   d. $m\widehat{VU}$ **35**

4. Find the measure of each arc of a circle that is circumscribed about the polygon.

   a. an equilateral triangle **120**   b. a regular pentagon **72**

   c. a regular hexagon **60**   d. a regular decagon **36**

   e. a regular dodecagon **30**   f. a regular n-gon $\dfrac{360}{n}$

Remember What You Learned

5. Some students have trouble distinguishing between *inscribed* and *circumscribed* figures. What is an easy way to remember which is which? **Sample answer: The *inscribed* figure is *inside* the circle.**

NAME _____ DATE _____ PERIOD _____

10-3 Study Guide and Intervention *(continued)*

Arcs and Chords

Arcs and Chords Points on a circle determine both chords and arcs. Several properties are related to points on a circle.

- In a circle or in congruent circles, two minor arcs are congruent if and only if their corresponding chords are congruent.

- If all the vertices of a polygon lie on a circle, the polygon is said to be **inscribed** in the circle and the circle is **circumscribed** about the polygon.

$\overline{RS} \cong \overline{TV}$ if and only if $\overline{RS} \cong \overline{TV}$.
RSVT is inscribed in $\odot O$.
$\odot O$ is circumscribed about RSVT.

Example Trapezoid *ABCD* is inscribed in $\odot O$. If $\overline{AB} \cong \overline{BC} \cong \overline{CD}$ and $m\widehat{BC} = 50$, what is $m\widehat{APD}$?

Chords $\overline{AB}, \overline{BC},$ and $\overline{CD}$ are congruent, so $\widehat{AB}, \widehat{BC},$ and $\widehat{CD}$ are congruent. $m\widehat{BC} = 50$, so $m\widehat{AB} + m\widehat{BC} + m\widehat{CD} = 50 + 50 + 50 = 150$. Then $m\widehat{APD} = 360 - 150$ or 210.

Exercises

Each regular polygon is inscribed in a circle. Determine the measure of each arc that corresponds to a side of the polygon.

1. hexagon
   60

2. pentagon
   72

3. triangle
   120

4. square
   90

5. octagon
   45

6. 36-gon
   10

Determine the measure of each arc of the circle circumscribed about the polygon.

7.

$m\widehat{UT} = 120$
$m\widehat{TS} = 60$
$m\widehat{RS} = 120$
$m\widehat{RU} = 60$

8.

$m\widehat{TU} = 140$
$m\widehat{UV} = 140$
$m\widehat{TV} = 80$

9.

$m\widehat{RVU} = 180$
$m\widehat{UT} = 60$
$m\widehat{TS} = 60$
$m\widehat{SR} = 60$

NAME _____ DATE _____ PERIOD _____

10-3 Study Guide and Intervention *(continued)*

Arcs and Chords

Diameters and Chords

- In a circle, if a diameter is perpendicular to a chord, then it bisects the chord and its arc.

- In a circle or in congruent circles, two chords are congruent if and only if they are equidistant from the center.

If $\overline{WZ} \perp \overline{AB}$, then $\overline{AX} \cong \overline{XB}$ and $\overline{AW} \cong \overline{WB}$.
If $\overline{OX} = \overline{OY}$, then $\overline{AB} \cong \overline{RS}$.
If $\overline{AB} \cong \overline{RS}$, then $\overline{AB}$ and $\overline{RS}$ are equidistant from point O.

Example In $\odot O$, $\overline{CD} \perp \overline{OE}$, $OE = 15$, and $CD = 24$. Find x.

A diameter or radius perpendicular to a chord bisects the chord, so ED is half of $\overline{CD}$.

$ED = \frac{1}{2}(24)$
$= 12$

Use the Pythagorean Theorem to find x in $\triangle OED$.

$(OE)^2 + (ED)^2 = (OD)^2$ Pythagorean Theorem
$x^2 + 12^2 = 15^2$ Substitution
$x^2 + 144 = 225$ Multiply.
$x^2 = 81$ Subtract 144 from each side.
$x = 9$ Take the square root of each side.

Exercises

In $\odot P$, $CD = 24$ and $m\widehat{CY} = 45$. Find each measure.

1. AQ **12**
2. RC **12**
3. QB **12**
4. AB **24**
5. $m\widehat{DY}$ **45**
6. $m\widehat{AB}$ **90**
7. $m\widehat{AX}$ **45**
8. $m\widehat{XB}$ **45**
9. $m\widehat{CD}$ **90**

In $\odot G$, $DG = GU$ and $AC = RT$. Find each measure.

10. TU **4**
11. TR **8**
12. $m\widehat{TS}$ **53.13**
13. CD **4**
14. GD **3**
15. $m\widehat{AB}$ **53.13**

16. A chord of a circle 20 inches long is 24 inches from the center of a circle. Find the length of the radius. **26 inches**

Answers (Lesson 10–3)

10-3 Skills Practice

Arcs and Chords

In $\odot H$, $m\overline{RS} = 82$, $m\overline{TU} = 82$, $RS = 46$, and $\overline{TU} \cong \overline{RS}$. Find each measure.

1. TU 46

2. TK 23

3. MS 23

4. $m\angle HKU$ 90

5. $m\widehat{AS}$ 41

6. $m\widehat{AR}$ 41

7. $m\widehat{TD}$ 41

8. $m\widehat{DU}$ 41

The radius of $\odot Y$ is 34, $AB = 60$, and $m\widehat{AC} = 71$. Find each measure.

9. $m\widehat{BC}$ 71

10. $m\widehat{AB}$ 142

11. AD 30

12. BD 30

13. YD 16

14. DC 18

In $\odot X$, $LX = MX$, $XY = 58$, and $VW = 84$. Find each measure.

15. YZ 84

16. YM 42

17. MX 40

18. MZ 42

19. LV 42

20. LX 40

10-3 Practice

Arcs and Chords

In $\odot E$, $m\widehat{HQ} = 48$, $HI = JK$, and $JR = 7.5$. Find each measure.

1. $m\widehat{HI}$ 96

2. $m\widehat{QI}$ 48

3. $m\widehat{JK}$ 96

4. HI 15

5. PI 7.5

6. JK 15

The radius of $\odot N$ is 18, $NK = 9$, and $m\widehat{DE} = 120$. Find each measure.

7. $m\widehat{GE}$ 60

8. $m\angle HNE$ 60

9. $m\widehat{HEN}$ 30

10. HN 9

The radius of $\odot O = 32$, $\widehat{PQ} \cong \widehat{RS}$, and $PQ = 56$. Find each measure.

11. PB 28

12. OB $4\sqrt{15} \approx 15.49$

13. **MANDALAS** The base figure in a mandala design is a nine-pointed star. Find the measure of each arc of the circle circumscribed about the star. Each arc measures 40°.

14. BQ 28

16. RS 56

10-3 Word Problem Practice

Arcs and Chords

NAME _____ DATE _____ PERIOD _____

1. **HEXAGON** A hexagon is constructed as shown in the figure.

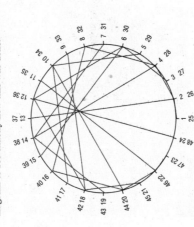

How many different chord lengths occur as side lengths of the hexagon?

2

2. **FENCING** A contractor is hired to build a fence around a circular park. The contractor traces out 10 radial lines each separated by 36°. He places a post where each line intersects the perimeter of the park. He then connects consecutive posts with a straight fence. The result is a fence that has the shape of a polygon with 10 sides. Is this polygon a regular decagon? Explain.

Yes. The arcs are equal, so the chords are equal.

3. **BIKE PATHS** Carl is planning to visit a circular park. The radius of the park is 8 miles. He is looking at a map of the park and sees that the park has five landmarks along its edge. The landmarks are connected by paths of equal length for biking. These paths form a regular pentagon inscribed in the circle. If Carl bikes along these paths to visit each landmark, how many miles will he bike?

47.02 mi

4. **CENTERS** Neil wants to find the center of a large circle drawn in the pavement of the schoolyard. He draws what he thinks is a diameter of the circle and then marks its midpoint and declares that he has found the center. His teacher comes by and asks Neil how he knows that the line he drew is really the diameter of the circle and not a smaller chord. Neil realizes that he does not know for sure. Explain what Neil can do to determine if it is an actual diameter.

Sample answer: Neil can draw a line perpendicular to the line he just drew through the mark he made. If the midpoint of the first line is also the midpoint of the second line, it is a diameter.

A TALE OF TWO TRIANGLES For Exercises 5 and 6, use the following information.

An equilateral triangle is inscribed in a circle with center O. The triangle is then rotated 30° to obtain another equilateral triangle inscribed in the circle.

5. What is $m\angle AOC$?

120°

6. Prove that the diameter through B is perpendicular to the diameter through C.

Because $m\overset{\frown}{AB} = 30$, $m\overset{\frown}{BC} = 120 - 30 = 90$, and $m\angle BOC = m\overset{\frown}{BC}$.

10-3 Enrichment

NAME _____ DATE _____ PERIOD _____

Patterns from Chords

Some beautiful and interesting patterns result if you draw chords to connect evenly spaced points on a circle. On the circle shown below, 24 points have been marked to divide the circle into 24 equal parts. Numbers from 1 to 48 have been placed beside the points. Study the diagram to see exactly how this was done.

1. Use your ruler and pencil to draw chords to connect numbered points as follows: 1 to 2, 2 to 4, 3 to 6, 4 to 8, and so on. Keep doubling until you have gone all the way around the circle. What kind of pattern do you get?

For figure, see above. The pattern is a heart-shaped figure.

2. Copy the original circle, points, and numbers. Try other patterns for connecting points. For example, you might try tripling the first number to get the number for the second endpoint of each chord. Keep special patterns for a possible class display.

See students' work.

Answers

Answers (Lesson 10–4)

Lesson Reading Guide (Page 26)

10-4 Lesson Reading Guide
Inscribed Angles

Get Ready for the Lesson

Read the introduction to Lesson 10-4 in your textbook.

- Why do you think regular hexagons are used rather than squares for the "hole" in a socket? **Sample answer: If a square were used, the points might be too sharp for the tool to work smoothly.**

- Why do you think regular hexagons are used rather than regular polygons with more sides? **Sample answer: If there are too many sides, the polygon would be too close to a circle, so the wrench might slip.**

Read the Lesson

1. Underline the correct word or phrase to form a true statement.

a. An angle whose vertex is on a circle and whose sides contain chords of the circle is called a(n) (central/<u>inscribed</u>/circumscribed) angle.

b. Every inscribed angle that intercepts a semicircle is a(n) (acute/<u>right</u>/obtuse) angle.

c. The opposite angles of an inscribed quadrilateral are (congruent/complementary/<u>supplementary</u>).

d. An inscribed angle that intercepts a major arc is a(n) (acute/right/<u>obtuse</u>) angle.

e. Two inscribed angles of a circle that intercept the same arc are (<u>congruent</u>/complementary/supplementary).

f. If a triangle is inscribed in a circle and one of the sides of the triangle is a diameter of the circle, the diameter is (the longest side of an acute triangle/<u>a leg of an isosceles triangle/the hypotenuse of a right triangle</u>).

2. Refer to the figure. Find each measure.

a. $m\angle ABC$ **90**   b. $m\widehat{CD}$ **118**

c. $m\widehat{AD}$ **62**   d. $m\angle BAC$ **34**

e. $m\angle BCA$ **56**   f. $m\widehat{AB}$ **112**

g. $m\widehat{BCD}$ **186**   h. $m\widehat{BDA}$ **248**

Remember What You Learned

3. A good way to remember a geometric relationship is to visualize it. Describe how you could make a sketch that would help you remember the relationship between the measure of an inscribed angle and the measure of its intercepted arc. **Sample answer: Draw a diameter of the circle to divide it into two semicircles. Inscribe an angle in one of the semicircles; this angle will intercept the other semicircle. From your sketch, you can see that the inscribed angle is a right angle. The measure of the semicircle arc is 180, so the measure of the inscribed angle is half the measure of its intercepted arc.**

Study Guide and Intervention (Page 27)

10-4 Study Guide and Intervention
Inscribed Angles

Inscribed Angles An **inscribed angle** is an angle whose vertex is on a circle and whose sides contain chords of the circle. In $\odot G$, inscribed $\angle DEF$ intercepts $\widehat{DF}$.

| **Inscribed Angle Theorem** | If an angle is inscribed in a circle, then the measure of the angle equals one-half the measure of its intercepted arc. |

Example In $\odot G$ above, $m\widehat{DF} = 90$. **Find $m\angle DEF$.**

$\angle DEF$ is an inscribed angle so its measure is half of the intercepted arc.

$m\angle DEF = \frac{1}{2}m\widehat{DF}$
$= \frac{1}{2}(90)$ or 45

Exercises

Use $\odot P$ for Exercises 1–10. In $\odot P$, $\overline{RS} \parallel \overline{TV}$ and $\overline{RT} \cong \overline{SV}$.

1. Name the intercepted arc for $\angle RTS$. **$\widehat{RS}$**

2. Name an inscribed angle that intercepts $\widehat{SV}$. **$\angle SRV$ or $\angle STV$**

In $\odot P$, $m\widehat{SV} = 120$ and $m\angle RPS = 76$. Find each measure.

3. $m\angle PRS$ **52**   **4.** $m\widehat{RSV}$ **196**

5. $m\widehat{RT}$ **120**   **6.** $m\angle RVT$ **60**

7. $m\angle QRS$ **60**   **8.** $m\angle STV$ **60**

9. $m\widehat{TV}$ **44**   **10.** $m\angle SVT$ **98**

Chapter 10

26

27

Glencoe Geometry

A12

10-4 Study Guide and Intervention *(continued)*
Inscribed Angles

Angles of Inscribed Polygons An inscribed polygon is one whose sides are chords of a circle and whose vertices are points on the circle. Inscribed polygons have several properties.

- If an angle of an inscribed polygon intercepts a semicircle, the angle is a right angle.
- If a quadrilateral is inscribed in a circle, then its opposite angles are supplementary.

If BCD is a semicircle, then $m\angle BCD = 90$.

For inscribed quadrilateral $ABCD$,
$m\angle A + m\angle C = 180$ and
$m\angle ABC + m\angle ADC = 180$.

Example In $\odot R$ above, $BC = 3$ and $BD = 5$. Find each measure.

a. $m\angle C$
$\angle C$ intercepts a semicircle. Therefore $\angle C$ is a right angle and $m\angle C = 90$.

b. CD
$\triangle BCD$ is a right triangle, so use the Pythagorean Theorem to find CD.
$(CD)^2 + (BC)^2 = (BD)^2$
$(CD)^2 + 3^2 = 5^2$
$(CD)^2 = 25 - 9$
$(CD)^2 = 16$
$CD = 4$

Exercises

Find the measure of each angle or segment for each figure.

1. $m\angle X, m\angle Y$
$m\angle X = 125;$ $m\angle Y = 60$

2. AD
6.5

3. $m\angle 1, m\angle 2$
$m\angle 1 = 50;$ $m\angle 2 = 90$

4. $m\angle 1, m\angle 2$
$m\angle 1 = 25;$ $m\angle 2 = 25$

5. AB, AC
$AB = 3;$ $AC = 6$

6. $m\angle 1, m\angle 2$
$m\angle 1 = 88;$ $m\angle 2 = 92$

10-4 Skills Practice
Inscribed Angles

In $\odot S$, $m\widehat{KL} = 80$, $m\widehat{LM} = 100$, and $m\widehat{MN} = 60$. Find the measure of each angle.

1. $m\angle 1$ 50
2. $m\angle 2$ 60
3. $m\angle 3$ 30
4. $m\angle 4$ 40
5. $m\angle 5$ 40
6. $m\angle 6$ 30

ALGEBRA Find the measure of each numbered angle for each figure.

7. $m\angle 1 = 5x - 2$, $m\angle 2 = 2x + 8$
$m\angle 1 = 58$, $m\angle 2 = 32$

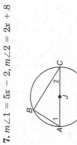

8. $m\angle 1 = 5x$, $m\angle 3 = 3x + 10$, $m\angle 4 = y + 7$, $m\angle 6 = 3y + 11$
$m\angle 1 = 50$, $m\angle 2 = 90$
$m\angle 3 = 40$, $m\angle 4 = 25$
$m\angle 5 = 90$, $m\angle 6 = 65$

Quadrilateral $RSTU$ is inscribed in $\odot P$ such that $m\widehat{STU} = 220$ and $m\angle S = 95$. Find each measure.

9. $m\angle R$ 110
10. $m\angle T$ 70
11. $m\angle U$ 85
12. $m\widehat{SRU}$ 140
13. $m\widehat{RUT}$ 190
14. $m\widehat{RST}$ 170

Answers *(Lesson 10–4)*

Left page

10-4 Practice

Inscribed Angles

In $\odot B$, $m\widehat{WX} = 104$, $m\widehat{WZ} = 88$, and $m\angle ZWY = 26$. Find the measure of each angle.

1. $m\angle 1$ **52**

2. $m\angle 2$ **26**

3. $m\angle 3$ **58**

4. $m\angle 4$ **44**

5. $m\angle 5$ **26**

6. $m\angle 6$ **52**

ALGEBRA Find the measure of each numbered angle for each figure.

7. $m\angle 1 = 5x + 2$, $m\angle 2 = 2x - 3$
$m\angle 3 = 7y - 1$, $m\angle 4 = 2y + 10$

$m\angle 1 = 67$, $m\angle 2 = 23$
$m\angle 3 = 62$, $m\angle 4 = 28$

8. $m\angle 1 = 4x - 7$, $m\angle 2 = 2x + 11$,
$m\angle 3 = 5y - 14$, $m\angle 4 = 3y + 8$

$m\angle 1 = 29$, $m\angle 2 = 29$
$m\angle 3 = 41$, $m\angle 4 = 41$

Quadrilateral *EFGH* is inscribed in $\odot N$ such that $m\widehat{FG} = 97$, $m\widehat{GH} = 117$, and $m\widehat{EHG} = 164$. Find each measure.

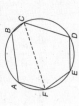

9. $m\angle E$ **107**

10. $m\angle F$ **82**

11. $m\angle G$ **73**

12. $m\angle H$ **98**

13. **PROBABILITY** In $\odot V$, point *C* is randomly located so that it does not coincide with points *R* or *S*. If $m\widehat{RS} = 140$, what is the probability that $m\angle RCS = 70$?

$\dfrac{11}{18}$

Right page

10-4 Word Problem Practice

Inscribed Angles

1. **ARENA** A circus arena is lit by five lights equally spaced around the perimeter.

What is $m\angle 1$?
72°

2. **FIELD OF VIEW** The figure shows a top view of two people in front of a very tall rectangular wall. The wall makes a chord of a circle that passes through both people.

Which person has more of their horizontal field of vision blocked by the wall?
Neither; the same amount of the field of vision is blocked for both viewers.

3. **RHOMBI** Paul is interested in circumscribing a circle around a rhombus that is not a square. He is having great difficulty doing so. Can you help him? Explain.
No, because it's impossible to do. Opposite angles of a rhombus are congruent, and if the rhombus is inscribed in a circle, the measures of the angles must add up to 180. This would imply that all of the angles are 90°. A rhombus with right angles can only be a square.

4. **STREETS** Three kilometers separate the intersections of Cross and Upton and Cross and Hope.

What is the distance between the intersection of Upton and Hope and the point midway between the intersections of Upton and Cross and Cross and Hope?
1.5 km

INSCRIBED HEXAGONS For Exercises 5 and 6, use the following information.

You will prove that the sum of the measures of alternate interior angles in an inscribed hexagon is 360.

5. How are $\angle A$ and $\angle BCF$ related? Similarly, how are $\angle E$ and $\angle DCF$ related?
They are supplementary.

6. Show that $m\angle A + m\angle BCD + m\angle E = 360°$.
$m\angle A + m\angle BCD + m\angle E =$
$m\angle A + m\angle BCF + m\angle DCF + m\angle E$
$= 180 + 180 = 360$

NAME _____ DATE _____ PERIOD _____

10-4 Enrichment

Formulas for Regular Polygons

Suppose a regular polygon of n sides is inscribed in a circle of radius r. The figure shows one of the isosceles triangles formed by joining the endpoints of one of each side of the polygon to the center C of the circle. In the figure, s is the length of each side of the regular polygon, and a is the length of the segment from C perpendicular to $\overline{AB}$.

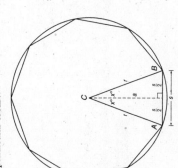

Use your knowledge of triangles and trigonometry to solve the following problems.

1. Find a formula for x in terms of the number of sides n of the polygon.

   $x = \dfrac{180°}{n}$

2. Find a formula for s in terms of the number of n and r. Use trigonometry.

   $s = 2r \sin\left(\dfrac{180°}{n}\right)$

3. Find a formula for a in terms of n and r. Use trigonometry.

   $a = r \cos\left(\dfrac{180°}{n}\right)$

4. Find a formula for the *perimeter* of the regular polygon in terms of n and r.

   $\text{perimeter} = 2nr \sin\left(\dfrac{180°}{n}\right)$

NAME _____ DATE _____ PERIOD _____

10-5 Lesson Reading Guide

Tangents

Get Ready for the Lesson

Read the introduction to Lesson 10-5 in your textbook.

How is the hammer throw event related to the mathematical concept of a tangent line?
Sample answer: When the hammer is released, its initial path is a good approximation of a tangent line to the circular path around which it was traveling just before it was released.

Read the Lesson

1. Refer to the figure. Name each of the following.

   a. two lines that are tangent to ⊙P $\overleftrightarrow{RQ}$ and $\overleftrightarrow{RS}$

   b. two points of tangency Q, S

   c. two chords of the circle $\overline{UQ}$ and $\overline{US}$

   d. three radii of the circle $\overline{PQ}, \overline{PS},$ and $\overline{PT}$

   e. two right angles $\angle PQR$ and $\angle PSR$

   f. two congruent right triangles $\triangle PQR$ and $\triangle PSR$

   g. the hypotenuse or hypotenuses in the two congruent right triangles $\overline{PR}$

   h. two congruent central angles $\angle QPT$ and $\angle SPT$

   i. two congruent minor arcs $\overset{\frown}{QT}$ and $\overset{\frown}{ST}$

   j. an inscribed angle $\angle QUS$

2. Explain the difference between an *inscribed polygon* and a *circumscribed polygon*. Use the words *vertex* and *tangent* in your explanation.
   Sample answer: If a polygon is *inscribed* in a circle, every vertex of the polygon lies on the circle. If a polygon is *circumscribed* about a circle, every side of the polygon is tangent to the circle.

Remember What You Learned

3. A good way to remember a mathematical term is to relate it to a word or expression that is used in a nonmathematical way. Sometimes a word or expression used in English is derived from a mathematical term. What does it mean to "go off on a tangent," and how is this meaning related to the geometric idea of a *tangent* line?
   Sample answer: To "go off on a tangent" means to suddenly change the subject when you are talking or writing. You can visualize this as being like a tangent line "going off" from a circle as you go farther from the point of tangency.

Answers

Answers (Lesson 10–5)

Right page (first study guide)

NAME _____ DATE _____ PERIOD _____

10-5 Study Guide and Intervention (continued)

Tangents

Circumscribed Polygons When a polygon is circumscribed about a circle, all of the sides of the polygon are tangent to the circle.

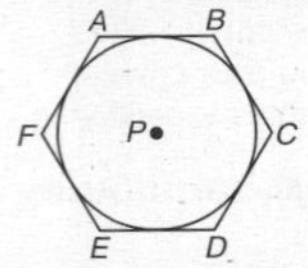

Hexagon *ABCDEF* is circumscribed about ⊙*P*.
$\overline{AB}, \overline{BC}, \overline{CD}, \overline{DE}, \overline{EF},$ and $\overline{FA}$ are tangent to ⊙*P*.

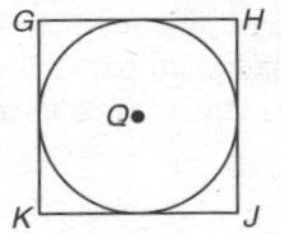

Square *GHJK* is circumscribed about ⊙*Q*.
$\overline{GH}, \overline{JH}, \overline{JK},$ and $\overline{KG}$ are tangent to ⊙*Q*.

Example △*ABC* is circumscribed about ⊙*O*.
Find the perimeter of △*ABC*.

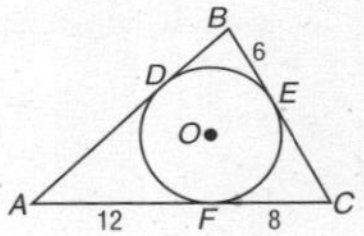

△*ABC* is circumscribed about ⊙*O*, so points *D*, *E*, and *F* are points of tangency. Therefore $AD = AF, BE = BD,$ and $CF = CE$.

$P = AD + AF + BE + BD + CF + CE$
$ = 12 + 12 + 6 + 6 + 8 + 8$
$ = 52$

The perimeter is 52 units.

Exercises

Find *x*. Assume that segments that appear to be tangent are tangent.

1.

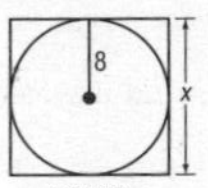

square

16

2.

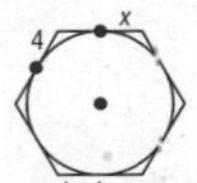

regular hexagon

4

3.

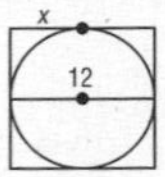

square

6

4.

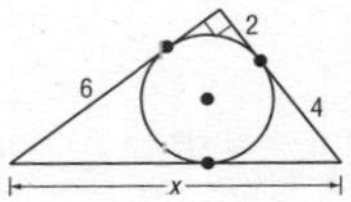

10

5.

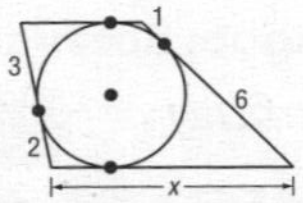

8

6.

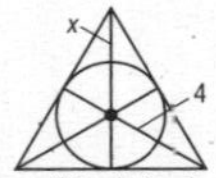

equilateral triangle

4

35

Chapter 10   *Glencoe Geometry*

Left page (second study guide)

NAME _____ DATE _____ PERIOD _____

10-5 Study Guide and Intervention (continued)

Tangents

Tangents A tangent to a circle intersects the circle in exactly one point, called the **point of tangency**. There are three important relationships involving tangents.

- If a line is tangent to a circle, then it is perpendicular to the radius drawn to the point of tangency.
- If a line is perpendicular to a radius of a circle at its endpoint on the circle, then the line is a tangent to the circle.
- If two segments from the same exterior point are tangent to a circle, then they are congruent.

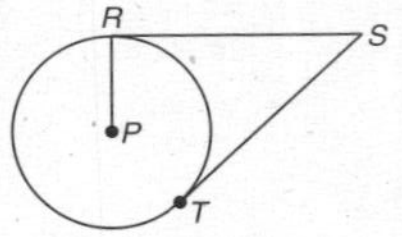

$\overline{RP} \perp \overline{SR}$ if and only if $\overline{SR}$ is tangent to ⊙*P*.

If $\overline{SR}$ and $\overline{ST}$ are tangent to ⊙*P*, then $\overline{SR} \cong \overline{ST}$.

Example $\overline{AB}$ **is tangent to ⊙*C*. Find *x*.**

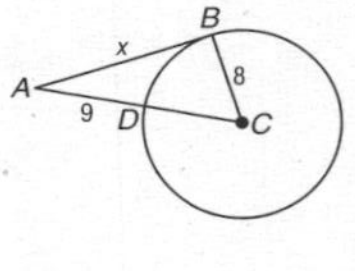

$\overline{AB}$ is tangent to ⊙*C*, so $\overline{AB}$ is perpendicular to radius $\overline{BC}$. $\overline{CD}$ is a radius, so $CD = 8$ and $AC = 9 + 8$ or 17. Use the Pythagorean Theorem with right △*ABC*.

$(AB)^2 + (BC)^2 = (AC)^2$ Pythagorean Theorem
$x^2 + 8^2 = 17^2$ Substitution
$x^2 + 64 = 289$ Multiply.
$x^2 = 225$ Subtract 64 from each side.
$x = 15$ Take the positive square root of each side.

Exercises

Find *x*. Assume that segments that appear to be tangent are tangent.

1.

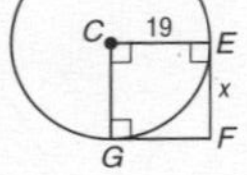

19

2.

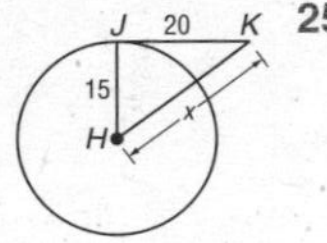

25

3.

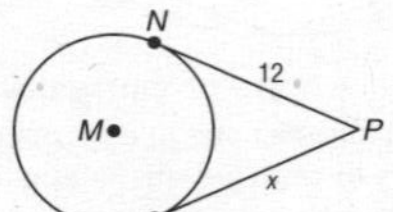

12

4.

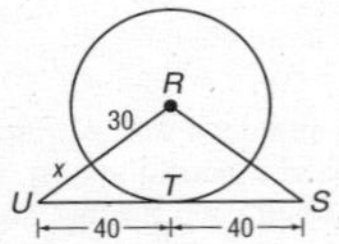

20

5.

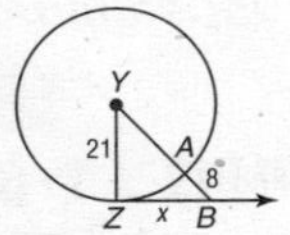

20

6.

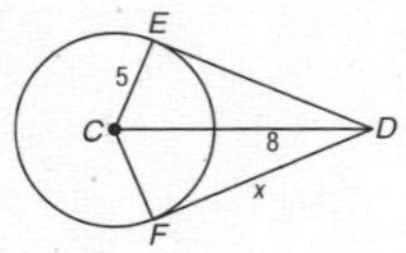

12

34

Chapter 10   *Glencoe Geometry*

Left worksheet

NAME _____ DATE _____ PERIOD _____

10-5 Skills Practice
Tangents

Determine whether each segment is tangent to the given circle.

1. $\overline{HI}$

yes

2. $\overline{AB}$

no

Find x. Assume that segments that appear to be tangent are tangent.

3.

$3x - 6$, $x + 10$

8

4.

$4x + 2$, $2x + 8$

3

5.

8, x, 17

15

6.

x, 24, 10

26

Find the perimeter of each polygon for the given information. Assume that segments that appear to be tangent are tangent.

7. $QT = 4$, $PT = 9$, $SR = 13$

52 units

8. $HIJK$ is a rhombus, $SI = 5$, $HR = 13$

72 units

Chapter 10   **36**   *Glencoe Geometry*

Right worksheet

NAME _____ DATE _____ PERIOD _____

10-5 Practice
Tangents

Determine whether each segment is tangent to the given circle.

1. $\overline{MP}$

20, 21, 28

no

2. $\overline{QR}$

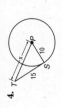
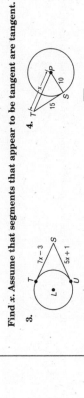

50, 48, 14

yes

Find x. Assume that segments that appear to be tangent are tangent.

3.

$7x - 3$, $5x + 1$

2

4.

x, 15, 10

$5\sqrt{13}$

Find the perimeter of each polygon for the given information. Assume that segments that appear to be tangent are tangent.

5. $CD = 52$, $CU = 18$, $TB = 12$

128 units

6. $KG = 32$, $HG = 56$

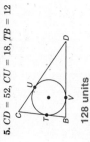

154 units

CLOCKS For Exercises 7 and 8, use the following information.
The design shown in the figure is that of a circular clock face inscribed in a triangular base. AF and FC are equal.

7. Find AB. **9.5 in.**

8. Find the perimeter of the clock. **34 in.**

Chapter 10   **37**   *Glencoe Geometry*

Answers (Lesson 10–5)

NAME _____ DATE _____ PERIOD _____

10-5 Word Problem Practice

Tangents

1. CANALS The concrete canal in Landtown is shaped like a "V" at the bottom. One day, Maureen accidentally dropped a cylindrical tube as she was walking and it rolled to the bottom of the dried out concrete canal. The figure shows a cross section of the tube at the bottom of the canal.

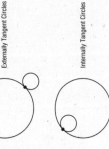

Compare the lengths *AV* and *BV*.
They are equal.

2. PACKAGING Taylor packed a sphere inside a cubic box. He had painted the sides of the box black before putting the sphere inside. When the sphere was later removed, he discovered that the black paint had not completely dried and there were black marks on the sides of the sphere at the points of tangency with the sides of the box. If the black marks are used as the vertices of a polygon, what kind of polygon results?
a square

3. TRIANGLES A circle is inscribed in a 40°-60°-80° triangle. The points of tangency form the vertices of a triangle inscribed in the circle. What are the angles of the inscribed triangle?

50° , 60° , 70°

4. ROLLING A wheel is rolling down an incline. Twelve evenly spaced diameters form spokes of the wheel.

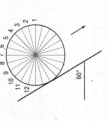

When spoke 2 is vertical, which spoke will be perpendicular to the incline?
spoke 10

DESIGN For Exercises 5 and 6, use the following information.
Amanda wants to make this design of circles inside an equilateral triangle.

5. What is the radius of the large circle to the nearest hundredth of an inch?
2.89 in.

6. What are the radii of the smaller circles to the nearest hundredth of an inch?
0.96 in.

NAME _____ DATE _____ PERIOD _____

10-5 Enrichment

Tangent Circles

Two circles in the same plane are **tangent circles** if they have exactly one point in common. Tangent circles with no common interior points are **externally tangent**. If tangent circles have common interior points, then they are **internally tangent**. Three or more circles are **mutually tangent** if each pair of them is tangent.

Externally Tangent Circles

Internally Tangent Circles

1. Make sketches to show all possible positions of three mutually tangent circles.

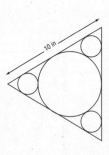

2. Make sketches to show all possible positions of four mutually tangent circles.

3. Make sketches to show all possible positions of five mutually tangent circles.

4. Write a conjecture about the number of possible positions for *n* mutually tangent circles if *n* is a whole number greater than four.
Possible answer: For *n* > 4, there are $\frac{n}{2}$ positions if *n* is even and $\frac{1}{2}(n + 1)$ positions if *n* is odd.

Answers (Lesson 10–5)

NAME _____ DATE _____ PERIOD _____

10-5 Graphing Calculator Activity
Cabri Junior: Exploring Tangents

A line that intersects a circle in exactly one point is called a **tangent** to the circle. You can use Cabri Junior to explore some of the characteristics of tangents. Use the following steps to draw two lines that are tangent to a circle.

Step 1 Draw a circle.
- Select **F2 Circle.**
- Place the cursor on the left center part of the screen and press ENTER . You have established the center of the circle.
- Press the left arrow to increase the radius length of the circle. Press ENTER when the circle has a desirable radius.
- Select **F5 Alph-num** to label the center of the circle *C*.

Step 2 Place a point outside the circle.
- Select **F2 Point, Point.**
- Move the cursor outside the circle. Press ENTER to establish the point.
- Label the point *A*.

Step 3 Draw a tangent line.
- Select **F2 Line.**
- Draw a line through point *A* that intersects circle *C* in exactly one point.
- Label the point *T*.

Step 4 Draw a second tangent line.
- Repeat the procedure in Step 3 to draw another line through *A* that is tangent to circle *C*.
- Label the point *S*.

The lines drawn to the circle are tangents to the circle. *Note that these tangents are approximate, since it is difficult to find the exact point where the line touches the circle.*

Exercises

Use the measuring capabilities of Cabri Jr. to explore the characteristics of tangents.

1. Measure $\overline{AT}$ and $\overline{AS}$. **See students' work.**

2. Move point *A* closer to the circle. (Press CLEAR so the pointer becomes a black arrow. Move the pointer close to point *A* until the arrow becomes transparent and point *A* is blinking. Press ALPHA to change the arrow to a hand. Then move the point.) Adjust $\overline{AT}$ and $\overline{AS}$ accordingly. Make a conjecture about the measurements of $\overline{AT}$ and $\overline{AS}$. **Sample answer: The measures are equal.**

3. Use the Segment tool to draw radii $\overline{CT}$ and $\overline{CS}$. Measure $\angle CTA$ and $\angle CSA$. **See students' work.**

4. Make a conjecture about the angles formed by a radius and a tangent to a circle. **They are right angles.**

Chapter 10   40   *Glencoe Geometry*

NAME _____ DATE _____ PERIOD _____

10-5 Geometer's Sketchpad Activity
Exploring Tangents

A line that intersects a circle in exactly one point is called a **tangent** to the circle. You can use The Geometer's Sketchpad to explore some of the characteristics of tangents. Use the following steps to draw two lines that are tangent to a circle.

Step 1: Use the Compass tool to draw a circle. Choose the Compass tool in the Tool Box. Then move the pointer to the sketch plane, where it becomes a circle. Position the pointer anywhere on the sketch plane to locate the center of the circle. Then click and drag the pointer until the circle has the desired radius. Release the mouse button to complete the circle. Label the center of the circle *C*.

Step 2: Next, use the Point tool to draw a point outside the circle. Label the point *A*.

Step 3: Use the Line tool to draw a line through point *A* that intersects circle *C* in exactly one point. Label the point of intersection *T*.

Step 4: Repeat the procedure in Step 3 to draw another line through point *A* that is tangent to circle *C* at point *S*.

The lines drawn to the circle are tangents to the circle. *Note that these tangents are approximate, since it is difficult to find the exact point where the line touches the circle.*

Exercises

Use the measuring capabilities of The Geometer's Sketchpad to explore the characteristics of tangents.

1. Measure $\overline{AT}$ and $\overline{AS}$. **See students' work.**

2. Move point *A* closer to the circle. Adjust $\overline{AT}$ and $\overline{AS}$ accordingly. Make a conjecture about the measurements of $\overline{AT}$ and $\overline{AS}$. **Sample answer: The measures are equal.**

3. Use the Segment tool to draw radii $\overline{CT}$ and $\overline{CS}$. Measure $\angle CTA$ and $\angle CSA$. **See students' work.**

4. Make a conjecture about the angles formed by a radius and a tangent to a circle. **They are right angles.**

Chapter 10   41   *Glencoe Geometry*

Answers

Left Page (42)

10-6 Lesson Reading Guide

Secants, Tangents, and Angle Measures

Get Ready for the Lesson

Read the introduction to Lesson 10-6 in your textbook.

- How would you describe $\angle C$ in the figure in your textbook?
  Sample answer: $\angle C$ is an inscribed angle in the circle that represents the raindrop.

- When you see a rainbow, where is the sun in relation to the circle of which the rainbow is an arc? **Sample answer: behind you and opposite the center of the circle**

Read the Lesson

1. Underline the correct word to form a true statement.

   a. A line can intersect a circle in at most (one/**two**/three) points.

   b. A line that intersects a circle in exactly two points is called a (tangent/**secant**/radius).

   c. A line that intersects a circle in exactly one point is called a (**tangent**/secant/chord).

   d. Every secant of a circle contains a (radius/tangent/**chord**).

2. Determine whether each statement is *always*, *sometimes*, or *never* true.

   a. A secant of a circle passes through the center of the circle. **sometimes**

   b. A tangent to a circle passes through the center of the circle. **never**

   c. A secant-secant angle is a central angle of the circle. **sometimes**

   d. A vertex of a secant-tangent angle is a point on the circle. **sometimes**

   e. A secant-tangent angle passes through the center of the circle. **sometimes**

   f. The vertex of a tangent-tangent angle is a point on the circle. **never**

   g. If one side of a secant-tangent angle passes through the center of the circle, the angle is a right angle. **sometimes**

   h. The measure of a secant-secant angle is one-half the positive difference of the measures of its intercepted arcs. **sometimes**

   i. The sum of the measures of the arcs intercepted by a tangent-tangent angle is 360. **always**

   j. The two arcs intercepted by a tangent-tangent angle are congruent. **never**

Remember What You Learned

3. Some students have trouble remembering the difference between a *secant* and a *tangent*. What is an easy way to remember which is which?
   Sample answer: A secant cuts a circle, while a tangent just touches it at one point. You can associate *tangent* with *touches* because they both start with *t*. Then associate *secant* with *cuts*.

Right Page (43)

10-6 Study Guide and Intervention

Secants, Tangents, and Angle Measures

Intersections On or Inside a Circle A line that intersects a circle in exactly two points is called a **secant**. The measures of angles formed by secants and tangents are related to intercepted arcs.

- If two secants intersect in the interior of a circle, then the measure of the angle formed is one-half the sum of the measure of the arcs intercepted by the angle and its vertical angle.

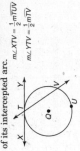

$$m\angle 1 = \frac{1}{2}(m\widehat{PR} + m\widehat{QS})$$

- If a secant and a tangent intersect at the point of tangency, then the measure of each angle formed is one-half the measure of its intercepted arc.

$$m\angle XTV = \frac{1}{2}m\widehat{TUV}$$
$$m\angle YTV = \frac{1}{2}m\widehat{TV}$$

Example 1   Find x.

The two secants intersect inside the circle, so x is equal to one-half the sum of the measures of the arcs intercepted by the angle and its vertical angle.

$$x = \frac{1}{2}(30 + 55)$$
$$= \frac{1}{2}(85)$$
$$= 42.5$$

Example 2   Find y.

The secant and the tangent intersect at the point of tangency, so the measure of the angle is one-half the measure of its intercepted arc.

$$y = \frac{1}{2}(168)$$
$$= 84$$

Exercises

Find each measure.

1. $m\angle 1$ **46**

2. $m\angle 2$ **46**

3. $m\angle 3$ **110**

4. $m\angle 4$ **30**

5. $m\angle 5$ **70**

6. $m\angle 6$ **100**

NAME _____ DATE _____ PERIOD _____

10-6 Skills Practice

Secants, Tangents, and Angle Measures

Find each measure.

1. $m\angle 1$

53

2. $m\angle 2$

137

3. $m\angle 3$

99

4. $m\angle 4$

118

5. $m\angle 5$

122

6. $m\angle 6$

66

Find x. Assume that any segment that appears to be tangent is tangent.

7.

40

8.

12

9.

48

10.

45

11.

264

12.

146

NAME _____ DATE _____ PERIOD _____

10-6 Study Guide and Intervention (continued)

Secants, Tangents, and Angle Measures

Intersections Outside a Circle If secants and tangents intersect outside a circle, they form an angle whose measure is related to the intercepted arcs.

If two secants, a secant and a tangent, or two tangents intersect in the exterior of a circle, then the measure of the angle formed is one-half the positive difference of the measures of the intercepted arcs.

$\overline{PB}$ and $\overline{PE}$ are secants.

$m\angle P = \frac{1}{2}(m\overline{BE} - m\overline{AD})$

$\overline{QG}$ is a tangent. $\overline{QJ}$ is a secant.

$m\angle Q = \frac{1}{2}(m\overline{GKJ} - m\overline{GH})$

$\overline{RM}$ and $\overline{RN}$ are tangents.

$m\angle R = \frac{1}{2}(m\overline{MTN} - m\overline{MN})$

Example **Find $m\angle MPN$.**

$\angle MPN$ is formed by two secants that intersect in the exterior of a circle.

$m\angle MPN = \frac{1}{2}(m\overline{MN} - m\overline{RS})$

$\quad = \frac{1}{2}(34 - 18)$

$\quad = \frac{1}{2}(16)$ or 8

The measure of the angle is 8.

Exercises

Find each measure.

1. $m\angle 1$ 20

2. $m\angle 2$ 40

3. $m\angle 3$ 40

4. x 30

5. x 130

6. x 15

44

NAME _____ DATE _____ PERIOD _____

10-6 Word Problem Practice

Secants, Tangents, and Angle Measures

1. TELESCOPES Vanessa looked through her telescope at a mountainous landscape. The figure shows what she saw. Based on the view, approximately what angle does the side of the mountain that runs from A to B make with the horizontal? **60°**

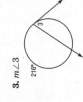

2. RADAR Two airplanes were tracked on radar. They followed the paths shown in the figure.

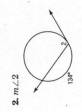

What is the acute angle between their flight paths? **67.5°**

3. EASELS Francisco is a painter. He places a circular canvas on his A-frame easel and carefully centers it. The apex of the easel is 30° and the measure of arc BC is 22°. What is the measure of arc AB? **128°**

4. FLYING When flying at an altitude of 5 miles, the lines of sight to the horizon looking north and south make about a 173.7° angle. How much of the longitude line directly under the plane is visible from 5 miles high?

173.7°

6.3

STAINED GLASS For Exercises 5 and 6, use the following information. Pablo made the stained glass window shown. He used an inscribed square and equilateral triangle for the design.

50°   70°
125°   95° 145°
55°   125° 20°
115°   55°
65°   35°   90°
155°   85°
80°   10°   95°
10°

5. Label the angle measures on the outer edge of the triangle. **See diagram.**

6. Label all of the arcs with their degree measure. **See diagram.**

NAME _____ DATE _____ PERIOD _____

10-6 Practice

Secants, Tangents, and Angle Measures

Find each measure.

1. $m\angle 1$
56°
146°
79

2. $m\angle 2$
134°
113

3. $m\angle 3$
216°
72

Find x. Assume that any segment that appears to be tangent is tangent.

7.
101°
39°
31

8.
15°
2x°
59°
14.5

9.
62°
x°
116°
60

10.
x°
63°
5x°
21

11.
52°
x°
128

12.
x°
37°
217

9. RECREATION In a game of kickball, Rickie has to kick the ball through a semicircular goal to score. If $m\widehat{XYZ} = 122$, at what angle must Rickie kick the ball to score? If $m\widehat{XY} = 58$ and the $m\widehat{XYZ} = 122$, at what angle must Rickie kick the ball to score? Explain.

goal
Y
X
Z
B (ball)

Rickie must kick the ball at an angle less than 32° since the measure of the angle from the ground that a tangent would make with the goal post is 32°.

NAME _____ DATE _____ PERIOD _____

10-6 Enrichment

Orbiting Bodies

The path of the Earth's orbit around the sun is elliptical. However, it is often viewed as circular.

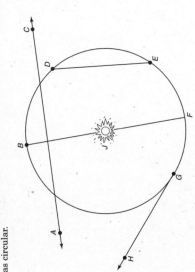

Use the drawing above of the Earth orbiting the sun to name the line or segment described. Then identify it as a *radius, diameter, chord, tangent,* or *secant* of the orbit.

1. the path of an asteroid $\overleftrightarrow{AC}$, secant

2. the distance between the Earth's position in July and the Earth's position in October $\overline{DE}$, chord

3. the distance between the Earth's position in December and the Earth's position in June $\overline{BF}$, diameter

4. the path of a rocket shot toward Saturn $\overrightarrow{GH}$, tangent

5. the path of a sunbeam $\overline{JB}$ or $\overline{JF}$, radius

6. If a planet has a moon, the moon circles the planet as the planet circles the sun. To visualize the path of the moon, cut two circles from a piece of cardboard, one with a diameter of 4 inches and one with a diameter of 1 inch.

Tape the larger circle firmly to a piece of paper. Poke a pencil point through the smaller circle, close to the edge. Roll the small circle around the outside of the large one. The pencil will trace out the path of a moon circling its planet. This kind of curve is called an epicycloid. To see the path of the planet around the sun, poke the pencil through the center of the small circle (the planet), and roll the small circle around the large one (the sun). **See students' work.**

NAME _____ DATE _____ PERIOD _____

10-7 Lesson Reading Guide

Special Segments in a Circle

Get Ready for the Lesson

Read the introduction to Lesson 10-7 in your textbook.

- What kinds of angles of the circle are formed at the points of the star? inscribed angles

- What is the sum of the measures of the five angles of the star? **180**

Read the Lesson

1. Refer to $\odot O$. Name each of the following.

   a. a diameter $\overline{AD}$

   b. a chord that is not a diameter $\overline{AB}$, $\overline{BF}$, or $\overline{AG}$

   c. two chords that intersect in the interior of the circle $\overline{AD}$ and $\overline{BF}$

   d. an exterior point E

   e. two secant segments that intersect in the exterior of the circle $\overline{EA}$ and $\overline{EB}$

   f. a tangent segment $\overline{ED}$

   g. a right angle $\angle ADE$

   h. an external secant segment $\overline{EF}$ or $\overline{EG}$

   i. a secant-tangent angle with vertex on the circle $\angle ADE$

   j. an inscribed angle $\angle BAD, \angle DAG, \angle BAG,$ or $\angle ABF$

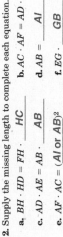

2. Supply the missing length to complete each equation.

   a. $BH \cdot HD = FH \cdot \underline{HC}$ b. $AC \cdot AF = AD \cdot \underline{AE}$

   c. $AD \cdot AE = AB \cdot \underline{AB}$ d. $AB = \underline{AI}$

   e. $AF \cdot AC = (AI$ or $AB)^2$ f. $EG \cdot \underline{GB} = FG \cdot GC$

Remember What You Learned

3. Some students find it easier to remember geometric theorems if they restate them in their own words. Restate Theorem 10.16 in a way that you find easier to remember. **Sample answer: Suppose you draw a secant to a circle through a point A outside the circle. Multiply the distances from point A to the points where the secant intersects the circle. The corresponding product will be the same for any other secant through point A to the same circle.**

Page 50

NAME _____ DATE _____ PERIOD _____

10-7 Study Guide and Intervention

Special Segments in a Circle

Segments Intersecting Inside a Circle If two chords intersect in a circle, then the products of the measures of the chords are equal.

$$a \cdot b = c \cdot d$$

Example Find x.

The two chords intersect inside the circle, so the products $AB \cdot BC$ and $EB \cdot BD$ are equal.

$AB \cdot BC = EB \cdot BD$

$6 \cdot x = 8 \cdot 3$ Substitution

$6x = 24$ Simplify.

$x = 4$ Divide each side by 6.

Exercises

Find x to the nearest tenth.

1. **9**

2. **6**

3. **10.7**

4. **2**

5. **3**

6. **4.9**

7. **2.2**

8. **4**

Page 51

NAME _____ DATE _____ PERIOD _____

10-7 Study Guide and Intervention (continued)

Special Segments in a Circle

Segments Intersecting Outside a Circle If secants and tangents intersect outside a circle, then two products are equal.

- If two secant segments are drawn to a circle from an exterior point, then the product of the measures of one secant segment and its external secant segment is equal to the product of the measures of the other secant segment and its external secant segment.

AC and AE are secant segments.
AB and AD are external secant segments.
$AC \cdot AB = AE \cdot AD$

- If a tangent segment and a secant segment are drawn to a circle from an exterior point, then the square of the measure of the tangent segment is equal to the product of the measures of the secant segment and its external secant segment.

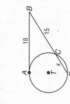

AB is a tangent segment.
AD is a secant segment.
AC is an external secant segment.
$(AB)^2 = AD \cdot AC$

Example Find x to the nearest tenth.

The tangent segment is $\overline{AB}$, the secant segment is $\overline{BD}$, and the external secant segment is $\overline{BC}$.

$(AB)^2 = BC \cdot BD$

$(18)^2 = 15(15 + x)$

$324 = 225 + 15x$

$99 = 15x$

$6.6 = x$

Exercises

Find x to the nearest tenth. Assume segments that appear to be tangent are tangent.

1. **2.8**

2. **19.3**

3. **7.7**

4. **2.0**

5. **1.0**

6. **5.0**

7. **37.3**

8. **13.2**

9. **4.0**

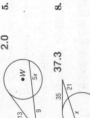

NAME _____ DATE _____ PERIOD _____

10-7 Practice

Special Segments in a Circle

Find *x* to the nearest tenth if necessary. Assume that segments that appear to be tangent are tangent.

1.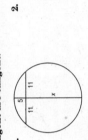
24.2

2.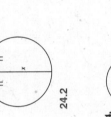
4.5

3.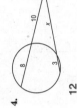
7.4

4.
12

5.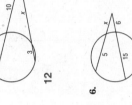
16

6.
9

7.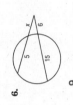
5.1

8.
30

9.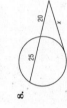
15.7

10. CONSTRUCTION An arch over an apartment entrance is 3 feet high and 9 feet wide. Find the radius of the circle containing the arc of the arch. **4.875 ft**

Chapter 10   53   *Glencoe Geometry*

NAME _____ DATE _____ PERIOD _____

10-7 Skills Practice

Special Segments in a Circle

Find *x* to the nearest tenth if necessary. Assume that segments that appear to be tangent are tangent.

1.
14

2.
13.5

3.
10

4.
6

5.
3

6.
6

7.
12

8.
10

9.
8

Chapter 10   52   *Glencoe Geometry*

Answers

10-7 Enrichment

The Nine-Point Circle

The figure below illustrates a surprising fact about triangles and circles. Given any △ABC, there is a circle that contains all of the following nine points:

(1) the midpoints K, L, and M of the sides of △ABC

(2) the points X, Y, and Z, where $\overline{AX}$, $\overline{BY}$, and $\overline{CZ}$ are the altitudes of △ABC

(3) the points R, S, and T which are the midpoints of the segments $\overline{AH}$, $\overline{BH}$, and $\overline{CH}$ that join the vertices of △ABC to the point H where the lines containing the altitudes intersect.

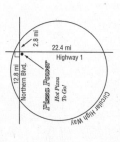

1. On a separate sheet of paper, draw an obtuse triangle ABC. Use your straightedge and compass to construct the circle passing through the midpoints of the sides. Be careful to make your construction as accurate as possible. Does your circle contain the other six points described above? **For constructions, see students' work; yes.**

2. In the figure you constructed for Exercise 1, draw $\overline{RK}$, $\overline{SL}$, and $\overline{TM}$. What do you observe? **The segments intersect at the center of the nine-point circle.**

10-7 Word Problem Practice

Special Segments in a Circle

1. **ICE SKATING** Ted skated through one of the face-off circles at a skating rink. His path through the circle is shown in the figure. Given that the face-off circle is 15 feet in diameter, what distance within the face-off circle did Ted travel? **13.8 ft**

2. **HORIZONS** Assume that Earth is a perfect sphere with a diameter of 7926 miles. From an altitude of a miles, how long is the horizon line h?

$$h = \sqrt{a(a + 7926)}$$

3. **AXLES** The figure shows the cross-section of an axle held in place by a triangular sleeve. A brake extends from the apex of the triangle. When the brake is extended 2.5 inches into the sleeve, it comes into contact with the axle. What is the diameter of the axle? **3.9 in.**

4. **ARCHEOLOGY** Scientists unearthed part of a circular wall. They made the measurements shown in the figure. Based on the information in the figure, what was the radius of the circle? **25.5 ft**

PIZZA DELIVERY For Exercises 5 and 6, use the following information.
Pizza Power is located at the intersection of Northern Boulevard and Highway 1 in a city with a circular highway running all the way around its outskirts. The radius of the circular highway is 13 miles. Pizza Power puts the map shown below on its take-out menus.

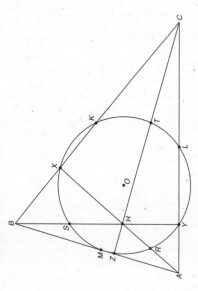

5. How many miles away is the Circular Highway from Pizza Power if you travel north on Highway 1? **1.6 mi**

6. The city builds a new road along the diameter of Circular Highway that passes through the intersection of Northern Boulevard and Highway 1. Along this new road, about how many miles is it (the shorter way) to the Circular Highway from Pizza Power? **about 1.46 mi**

NAME _____ DATE _____ PERIOD _____

10-8 Study Guide and Intervention
Equations of Circles

Equation of a Circle A circle is the locus of points in a plane equidistant from a given point. You can use this definition to write an equation of a circle.

Standard Equation of a Circle	An equation for a circle with center at (h, k) and a radius of r units is $(x - h)^2 + (y - k)^2 = r^2$.

Example Write an equation for a circle with center $(-1, 3)$ and radius 6.

Use the formula $(x - h)^2 + (y - k)^2 = r^2$ with $h = -1$, $k = 3$, and $r = 6$.

$(x - h)^2 + (y - k)^2 = r^2$ Equation of a circle
$(x - (-1))^2 + (y - 3)^2 = 6^2$ Substitution
$(x + 1)^2 + (y - 3)^2 = 36$ Simplify.

Exercises

Write an equation for each circle.

1. center at $(0, 0)$, $r = 8$
$x^2 + y^2 = 64$

2. center at $(-2, 3)$, $r = 5$
$(x + 2)^2 + (y - 3)^2 = 25$

3. center at $(2, -4)$, $r = 1$
$(x - 2)^2 + (y + 4)^2 = 1$

4. center at $(-1, -4)$, $r = 2$
$(x + 1)^2 + (y + 4)^2 = 4$

5. center at $(-2, -6)$, diameter = 8
$(x + 2)^2 + (y + 6)^2 = 16$

6. center at $\left(-\frac{1}{2}, \frac{1}{4}\right)$, $r = \sqrt{3}$
$\left(x + \frac{1}{2}\right)^2 + \left(y - \frac{1}{4}\right)^2 = 3$

7. center at the origin, diameter = 4
$x^2 + y^2 = 4$

8. center at $\left(1, -\frac{5}{8}\right)$, $r = \sqrt{5}$
$(x - 1)^2 + \left(y + \frac{5}{8}\right)^2 = 5$

9. Find the center and radius of a circle with equation $x^2 + y^2 = 20$.
center $(0, 0)$; radius $2\sqrt{5}$

10. Find the center and radius of a circle with equation $(x + 4)^2 + (y + 3)^2 = 16$.
center $(-4, -3)$; radius 4

NAME _____ DATE _____ PERIOD _____

10-8 Lesson Reading Guide
Equations of Circles

Get Ready for the Lesson

Read the introduction to Lesson 10-8 in your textbook.

In a series of concentric circles, what is the same about all the circles, and what is different?
Sample answer: They all have the same center, but different radii.

Read the Lesson

1. Identify the center and radius of each circle.
a. $(x - 2)^2 + (y - 3)^2 = 16$ (2, 3); 4
b. $(x + 1)^2 + (y + 5)^2 = 9$ (−1, −5); 3
c. $x^2 + y^2 = 49$ (0, 0); 7
d. $(x - 8)^2 + (y + 1)^2 = 36$ (8, −1); 6
e. $x^2 + (y - 10)^2 = 144$ (0, 10); 12
f. $(x + 3)^2 + y^2 = 5$ (−3, 0); $\sqrt{5}$

2. Write an equation for each circle.
a. center at origin, $r = 8$ $x^2 + y^2 = 64$
b. center at (3, 9), $r = 1$ $(x - 3)^2 + (y - 9)^2 = 1$
c. center at (−5, −6), $r = 10$ $(x + 5)^2 + (y + 6)^2 = 100$
d. center at (0, −7), $r = 7$ $x^2 + (y + 7)^2 = 49$
e. center at (12, 0), $d = 12$ $(x - 12)^2 + y^2 = 36$
f. center at (−4, 8), $d = 22$ $(x + 4)^2 + (y - 8)^2 = 121$
g. center at (4.5, −3.5), $r = 1.5$ $(x - 4.5)^2 + (y + 3.5)^2 = 2.25$
h. center at (0, 0), $r = \sqrt{13}$ $x^2 + y^2 = 13$

3. Write an equation for each circle.
a. $(x + 3)^2 + (y - 3)^2 = 4$
b. $x^2 + (y + 2)^2 = 9$
c. $x^2 + y^2 = 9$
d. $(x - 1)^2 + y^2 = 9$

Remember What You Learned

4. A good way to remember a new mathematical formula or equation is to relate it to one you already know. How can you use the Distance Formula to help you remember the standard equation of a circle? **Sample answer: Use the Distance Formula to find the distance between the center (h, k) and a general point (x, y) on the circle. Square each side to obtain the standard equation of a circle.**

Answers

10-8 Skills Practice

Equations of Circles

Write an equation for each circle.

1. center at origin, $r = 6$
$x^2 + y^2 = 36$

2. center at $(0, 0)$, $r = 2$
$x^2 + y^2 = 4$

3. center at $(4, 3)$, $r = 9$
$(x - 4)^2 + (y - 3)^2 = 81$

4. center at $(7, 1)$, $d = 24$
$(x - 7)^2 + (y - 1)^2 = 144$

5. center at $(-5, 2)$, $r = 4$
$(x + 5)^2 + (y - 2)^2 = 16$

6. center at $(6, -8)$, $d = 10$
$(x - 6)^2 + (y + 8)^2 = 25$

7. a circle with center at $(8, 4)$ and a radius with endpoint $(0, 4)$
$(x - 8)^2 + (y - 4)^2 = 64$

8. a circle with center at $(-2, -7)$ and a radius with endpoint $(0, 7)$
$(x + 2)^2 + (y + 7)^2 = 200$

9. a circle with center at $(-3, 9)$ and a radius with endpoint $(1, 9)$
$(x + 3)^2 + (y - 9)^2 = 16$

10. a circle whose diameter has endpoints $(-3, 0)$ and $(3, 0)$
$x^2 + y^2 = 9$

Graph each equation.

11. $x^2 + y^2 = 16$

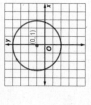

12. $(x - 1)^2 + (y - 4)^2 = 9$

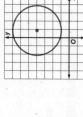

10-8 Study Guide and Intervention (continued)

Equations of Circles

Graph Circles If you are given an equation of a circle, you can find information to help you graph the circle.

Example Graph $(x + 3)^2 + (y - 1)^2 = 9$.
Use the parts of the equation to find (h, k) and r.

$(x - h)^2 + (y - k)^2 = r^2$
$(x - h)^2 = (x + 3)^2$ $(y - k)^2 = (y - 1)^2$ $r^2 = 9$
$x - h = x + 3$ $y - k = y - 1$ $r = 3$
$-h = 3$ $-k = -1$
$h = -3$ $k = 1$

The center is at $(-3, 1)$ and the radius is 3. Graph the center. Use a compass set at a radius of 3 grid squares to draw the circle.

Exercises

Graph each equation.

1. $x^2 + y^2 = 16$

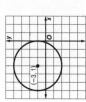

2. $(x - 2)^2 + (y - 1)^2 = 9$

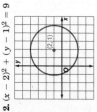

3. $(x + 2)^2 + y^2 = 16$

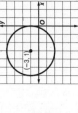

4. $(x + 1)^2 + (y - 2)^2 = 6.25$

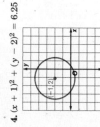

5. $\left(x + \frac{1}{2}\right)^2 + \left(y - \frac{1}{4}\right)^2 = 4$

6. $x^2 + (y - 1)^2 = 9$

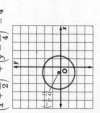

NAME _____ DATE _____ PERIOD _____

10-8 Practice

Equations of Circles

Write an equation for each circle.

1. center at origin, $r = 7$

$x^2 + y^2 = 49$

2. center at $(0, 0)$, $d = 18$

$x^2 + y^2 = 81$

3. center at $(-7, 11)$, $r = 8$

$(x + 7)^2 + (y - 11)^2 = 64$

4. center at $(12, -9)$, $d = 22$

$(x - 12)^2 + (y + 9)^2 = 121$

5. center at $(-6, -4)$, $r = \sqrt{5}$

$(x + 6)^2 + (y + 4)^2 = 5$

6. center at $(3, 0)$, $d = 28$

$(x - 3)^2 + y^2 = 196$

7. a circle with center at $(-5, 3)$ and a radius with endpoint $(2, 3)$

$(x + 5)^2 + (y - 3)^2 = 49$

8. a circle whose diameter has endpoints $(4, 6)$ and $(-2, 6)$

$(x - 1)^2 + (y - 6)^2 = 9$

Graph each equation.

9. $x^2 + y^2 = 4$

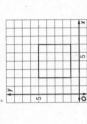

10. $(x + 3)^2 + (y - 3)^2 = 9$

11. EARTHQUAKES When an earthquake strikes, it releases seismic waves that travel in concentric circles from the epicenter of the earthquake. Seismograph stations monitor seismic activity and record the intensity and duration of earthquakes. Suppose a station determines that the epicenter of an earthquake is located about 50 kilometers from the station. If the station is located at the origin, write an equation for the circle that represents a possible epicenter of the earthquake. $x^2 + y^2 = 2500$

NAME _____ DATE _____ PERIOD _____

10-8 Word Problem Practice

Equations of Circles

1. DESIGN Arthur wants to write the equation of a circle that is inscribed in the square shown in the graph.

What is the equation of the desired circle?

$(x - 4)^2 + (y - 3)^2 = 4$

2. DRAFTING The design for a park is drawn on a coordinate graph. The perimeter of the park is modeled by the equation $(x - 3)^2 + (x - 7)^2 = 225$. Each unit on the graph represents 10 feet. What is the radius of the actual park?

150 ft

3. WALLPAPER The design of a piece of wallpaper consists of circles that can be modeled by the equation $(x - a)^2 + (y - b)^2 = 4$, for all even integers b. Sketch part of the wallpaper on a grid.

Sample answer:

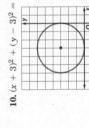

4. SECURITY RING A circular safety ring surrounds a top-secret laboratory. On one map of the laboratory grounds, the safety ring is given by the equation $x^2 + y^2 - 20x + 14y = 175$. Each unit on the map represents 1 mile. What is the radius of the safety ring?

18 mi

DISTANCE For Exercises 5-7, use the following information.

Cleo lives the same distance from the library, the post office, and her school. The table below gives the coordinates of these places on a map with a coordinate grid where one unit represents one yard.

Location	Coordinates
Library	$(-78, 202)$
Post Office	$(111, 193)$
School	$(202, -106)$

5. What are the coordinates of Cleo's home? Sketch the circle on a map locating all three places and Cleo's home.

$(7, -2)$

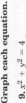

6. How far is Cleo's house from the places mentioned?

221 yd

7. Write an equation for the circle that passes through the library, post office, and school.

$(x - 7)^2 + (y + 2)^2 = 221^2$

NAME _____ DATE _____ PERIOD _____

10-8 Enrichment

Equations of Circles and Tangents

Recall that the circle whose radius is r and whose center has coordinates (h, k) is the graph of $(x - h)^2 + (y - k)^2 = r^2$. You can use this idea and what you know about circles and tangents to find an equation of the circle that has a given center and is tangent to a given line.

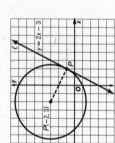

Use the following steps to find an equation for the circle that has center $C(-2, 3)$ and is tangent to the graph $y = 2x - 3$. Refer to the figure.

1. State the slope of the line ℓ that has equation $y = 2x - 3$.

   2

2. Suppose $\odot C$ with center $C(-2, 3)$ is tangent to line ℓ at point P. What is the slope of radius $\overline{CP}$?

   $-\dfrac{1}{2}$

3. Find an equation for the line that contains $\overline{CP}$.

   $y = -\dfrac{1}{2}x + 2$

4. Use your equation from Exercise 3 and the equation $y = 2x - 3$. At what point do the lines for these equations intersect? What are its coordinates?

   $P; (2, 1)$

5. Find the measure of radius $\overline{CP}$.

   $\sqrt{20}$ or $2\sqrt{5}$

6. Use the coordinate pair $C(-2, 3)$ and your answer for Exercise 5 to write an equation for $\odot C$.

   $(x - (-2))^2 + (y - 3)^2 = 20$ or $(x + 2)^2 + (y - 3)^2 = 20$

Chapter 10   62   Glencoe Geometry

Chapter 10 Assessment Answer Key

Quiz 1 *(Lessons 10–1 and 10–2)*
Page 65

1. _____8_____

2. _____40.84 in._____

3. _____73°_____

4. _____6.28 in._____

5. _____D_____

Quiz 2 *(Lessons 10–3 and 10–4)*
Page 65

1. _____70°_____

2. _____15 in._____

3. _____22_____

4. _____12 cm_____

5. _____21.77 cm_____

Quiz 3 *(Lessons 10–5 and 10–6)*
Page 66

1. _____$12\sqrt{3}$ ft_____

2. _____false_____

3. _____65°_____

4. _____77.5°_____

5. _____112.5°_____

Quiz 4 *(Lessons 10–7 and 10–8)*
Page 66

1. _____4_____

2. $x = \sqrt{21},\ y = \dfrac{17}{2}$

3. _____(−11, 13)_____

4. _____15_____

5.
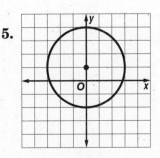

Mid-Chapter Test
Page 67

Part I

1. __A__

2. __J__

3. __B__

4. __H__

5. __B__

Part II

6. _____44°_____

7. _____120°_____

8. _____5 cm_____

9. _____8.5 in._____

10. _____87°_____

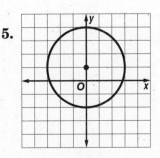

Answers

Chapter 10 Assessment Answer Key

1. false, inscribed
2. true
3. true
4. false, radius
5. false, minor arc
6. tangent
7. secant
8. tangent
9. semicircle
10. pi (π)

11. arcs in the same ⊙ or ≅ ⊙s that have the same measure

12. A polygon is circumscribed about a ⊙ if all of its sides are tangent to the ⊙.

1. A
2. H
3. D
4. G
5. B
6. H
7. A
8. H
9. B
10. F
11. D

12. G
13. C
14. G
15. D
16. J
17. B
18. G
19. B
20. J

B: 7

Chapter 10 Assessment Answer Key

Form 2A
Page 71

1. __A__

2. __G__

3. __C__

4. __F__

5. __C__

6. __G__

7. __C__

8. __J__

9. __D__

10. __F__

11. __D__

Page 72

12. __H__

13. __C__

14. __F__

15. __B__

16. __J__

17. __B__

18. __F__

19. __D__

20. __F__

B: _____10_____

Form 2B
Page 73

1. __B__

2. __H__

3. __C__

4. __F__

5. __C__

6. __F__

7. __B__

8. __G__

9. __C__

10. __F__

11. __B__

Page 74

12. __H__

13. __A__

14. __H__

15. __A__

16. __J__

17. __C__

18. __J__

19. __D__

20. __G__

B: ____outside____

Answers

Chapter 10 Assessment Answer Key

Form 2C
Page 75

1. _____ 2 in. _____

2. _____ radius = 5.5 in. and diameter = 11 in. _____

3. _____ 80° _____

4. _____ 15.71 units _____

5. _____ 7 _____

6. _____ 12 m _____

7. _____ 52 _____

8. _____ 36° _____

9. _____ $\dfrac{4}{5}$ _____

10. _____ 7 units _____

11. _____ 11 _____

Page 76

12. _____ $\dfrac{7}{3}$ _____

13. _____ 31° _____

14. _____ 41° _____

15. _____ 70° _____

16. _____ 100° _____

17. _____ $2\sqrt{2}$ _____

18. _____ $(x-3)^2 + (y-5)^2 = 26$ _____

19. _____ $(x+4)^2 + (y+9)^2 = 100$ _____

20.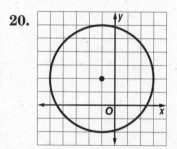

B: _____ $y = -\dfrac{4}{3}x + \dfrac{23}{3}$ _____

Chapter 10 Assessment Answer Key

Form 2D
Page 77

1. _____4_____

2. _____62.8 in._____

3. _____29_____

4. ___75.40 units___

5. _____90°_____

6. _____$\dfrac{29}{4}$_____

7. _____96_____

8. _____80°_____

9. _____$-\dfrac{3}{5}$_____

10. ____9 units____

11. _____11_____

Page 78

12. _____7_____

13. _____60°_____

14. _____70°_____

15. _____50°_____

16. _____110°_____

17. __$(x + 7)^2 +$__ $(y - 8)^2 = 81$

18. __$(x - 4)^2 +$__ $(y + 9)^2 = 116$

19. _____$3\sqrt{5}$_____

20.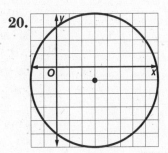

B: __$(-1, 2), (-1, -2)$__

Answers

Chapter 10 Assessment Answer Key

Form 3
Page 79

1. $3\sqrt{2}$ ft

2. 26.66 in.

3. 149°

4. 27 in.

5. $4\sqrt{6}$

6. 17 cm

7. 47

8. $\dfrac{\sqrt{2}}{2}$ ft

9. $\dfrac{10\sqrt{3}}{3}$

10. 4

11. 58

Page 80

12. 25°

13. 62.5°

14. 52.5°

15. 12

16. 2

17. $(0, 5), \left(\dfrac{300}{61}, \dfrac{55}{61}\right)$

18. $(x + 3)^2 + (y + 2)^2 = 9$

19. center: $(6, -7)$, radius: 9

20.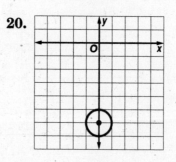

B: (5, 5)

Chapter 10 Assessment Answer Key

Extended-Response Test, Page 81
Scoring Rubric

Score	General Description	Specific Criteria
4	**Superior** A correct solution that is supported by well-developed, accurate explanations	• Shows thorough understanding of the concepts of *circles, arcs, chords, tangents, secants, inscribed and circumscribed polygons, and equations of circles.* • Uses appropriate strategies to solve problems. • Computations are correct. • Written explanations are exemplary. • Figures and graphs are accurate and appropriate. • Goes beyond requirements of some or all problems.
3	**Satisfactory** A generally correct solution, but may contain minor flaws in reasoning or computation	• Shows an understanding of the concepts of *circles, arcs, chords, tangents, secants, inscribed and circumscribed polygons, and equations of circles.* • Uses appropriate strategies to solve problems. • Computations are mostly correct. • Written explanations are effective. • Figures and graphs are mostly accurate and appropriate. • Satisfies all requirements of problems.
2	**Nearly Satisfactory** A partially correct interpretation and/or solution to the problem	• Shows an understanding of most of the concepts of *circles, arcs, chords, tangents, secants, inscribed and circumscribed polygons, and equations of circles.* • May not use appropriate strategies to solve problems. • Computations are mostly correct. • Written explanations are satisfactory. • Figures and graphs are mostly accurate. • Satisfies the requirements of most of the problems.
1	**Nearly Unsatisfactory** A correct solution with no supporting evidence or explanation	• Final computation is correct. • No written explanations or work shown to substantiate the final computation. • Figures and graphs may be accurate but lack detail or explanation. • Satisfies minimal requirements of some of the problems.
0	**Unsatisfactory** An incorrect solution indicating no mathematical understanding of the concept or task, or no solution is given	• Shows little or no understanding of most of the concepts of *circles, arcs, chords, tangents, secants, inscribed and circumscribed polygons, and equations of circles.* • Does not use appropriate strategies to solve problems. • Computations are incorrect. • Written explanations are unsatisfactory. • Figures and graphs are inaccurate or inappropriate. • Does not satisfy requirements of problems. • No answer given.

Answers

Chapter 10 Assessment Answer Key

Extended-Response Test, Page 81
Sample Answers

In addition to the scoring rubric found on page A37, the following sample answers may be used as guidance in evaluating open-ended assessment items.

1. 100 families were surveyed about the type of pet they own. The results are:

no pets	20	$\dfrac{20}{100} = \dfrac{x}{360}$	72°
dogs	30	$\dfrac{30}{100} = \dfrac{x}{360}$	108°
cats	25	$\dfrac{25}{100} = \dfrac{x}{360}$	90°
fish	15	$\dfrac{15}{100} = \dfrac{x}{360}$	54°
birds	10	$\dfrac{10}{100} = \dfrac{x}{360}$	36°

2. a. Arc length is the measure of the distance around part of a circle. It is a fraction of the circumference of the circle. Arc length is measured in centimeters or inches or feet, etc. Arc measure is the number of degrees in an arc. It is measured with a protractor.

  b. Yes. The arcs could have the same measure, for example 60, but could be arcs in circles with different radii. The arc in the circle with the greater radius would have a greater length.

3.

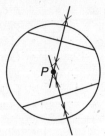

4. The measures decrease.

5. a. $(x - 2)^2 + (y + 3)^2 = 25$

  b. $B(-1, 1)$

  c. center: $(2, -3)$

  The slope of the segment, having endpoints at B and the point of tangency to the center, is $-\dfrac{4}{3}$.

  The slope of tangent line is $\dfrac{3}{4}$.

  equation: $y - 1 = \dfrac{3}{4}(x + 1)$ or

  $y = \dfrac{3}{4}x + \dfrac{7}{4}$

Chapter 10   **A38**   *Glencoe Geometry*

Copyright © Glencoe/McGraw-Hill, a division of The McGraw-Hill Companies, Inc.

Chapter 10 Assessment Answer Key

Standardized Test Practice
Page 82

Page 83

1. Ⓐ Ⓑ ● Ⓓ

2. Ⓕ ● Ⓗ Ⓙ

3. ● Ⓑ Ⓒ Ⓓ

4. ● Ⓖ Ⓗ Ⓙ

5. Ⓐ Ⓑ ● Ⓓ

6. Ⓕ ● Ⓗ Ⓙ

7. Ⓐ Ⓑ Ⓒ ●

8. ● Ⓖ Ⓗ Ⓙ

9. Ⓐ Ⓑ ● Ⓓ

10. Ⓕ ● Ⓗ Ⓙ

11. Ⓐ Ⓑ ● Ⓓ

12.

		7	4	.			
⓪	⓪	⓪	⓪		⓪	⓪	⓪
①	①	①	①		①	①	①
②	②	②	②		②	②	②
③	③	③	③		③	③	③
④	④	④	●		④	④	④
⑤	⑤	⑤	⑤		⑤	⑤	⑤
⑥	⑥	⑥	⑥		⑥	⑥	⑥
⑦	⑦	●	⑦		⑦	⑦	⑦
⑧	⑧	⑧	⑧		⑧	⑧	⑧
⑨	⑨	⑨	⑨		⑨	⑨	⑨

13.

		9	7	.			
⓪	⓪	⓪	⓪		⓪	⓪	⓪
①	①	①	①		①	①	①
②	②	②	②		②	②	②
③	③	③	③		③	③	③
④	④	④	④		④	④	④
⑤	⑤	⑤	⑤		⑤	⑤	⑤
⑥	⑥	⑥	⑥		⑥	⑥	⑥
⑦	⑦	⑦	●		⑦	⑦	⑦
⑧	⑧	⑧	⑧		⑧	⑧	⑧
⑨	⑨	●	⑨		⑨	⑨	⑨

Answers

Standardized Test Practice
Page 84

14. _____ $m\angle 1 = 13$

15. _____ $AB > BC$

16. _____ yes

17. _____ 20 cm

18. _____ true

19. _____ $DFHJB \sim PQRJH$

20. _____ $a = 2; b = 20$

21a. _____ $(x - 4)^2 + (y + 1)^2 = 144$

21b. _____ 24π

21c. _____ 144π